THE MANAGEMENT OF INTERNATIONAL OIL AND GAS HEALTH AND SAFETY

A GUIDE TO THE NEBOSH INTERNATIONAL TECHNICAL CERTIFICATE IN OIL AND GAS OPERATIONAL SAFETY

CONTRIBUTORS

Roger Passey, CMIOSH, MIIRSM
David Towlson, BSc, PhD, CMIOSH, AIEMA, MIfL, Cert Ed (PCET)
Richard Griffiths, PhD, MSc (Env Man), MEd, Cert Ed, GRSC (1st), CMIOSH, MIIRSM, AIEMA, FRSPH
Terry Robson, Bsc (Hons), PhD, CFIOSH, MRSC, CChem

ENDORSED BY

nebosh
Endorsed

This publication is endorsed by NEBOSH as offering high quality support for the delivery of NEBOSH qualifications.

NEBOSH endorsement does not imply that this publication is essential to achieve a NEBOSH qualification, nor does it mean that this is the only suitable publication available to support NEBOSH qualifications. No endorsed material will be used verbatim in setting any NEBOSH examination and all responsibility for content remains with the publisher.

Copies of official specifications for all NEBOSH qualifications may be found on the NEBOSH website – www.nebosh.org.uk

ACKNOWLEDGMENTS

RRC Intenational would like to thank the National Examination Board in Occupational Safety and Health (NEBOSH) for their co-operation in allowing us to reproduce extracts from their syllabus guides.

This publication contains public sector information published by the Health and Safety Executive and
licensed under the Open Government Licence v.10
(www.nationalarchives.gov.uk/doc/open-government-licence/).

Every effort has been made to trace copyright material and obtain permission to reproduce it. If there are any errors or omissions, RRC would welcome notification so that corrections may be incorporated in future reprints or editions of this material.

Whilst the information in this book is believed to be true and accurate at the date of going to press, neither the author nor the publisher can accept any legal responsibility or liability for any errors or omissions that may be made.

Contents

Contents

ELEMENT 4: FIRE PROTECTION AND EMERGENCY RESPONSE

ELEMENT 5: LOGISTICS AND TRANSPORT OPERATIONS

REVISION AND EXAMINATION

SUGGESTED ANSWERS

Introduction

COURSE STRUCTURE

This textbook has been designed to provide the reader with the core knowledge needed to successfully complete the NEBOSH International Technical Certificate in Oil and Gas Operational Safety, as well as providing a useful overview of health and safety management in the oil and gas industries. It follows the structure and content of the NEBOSH syllabus.

For more detailed information about how the syllabus is structured, visit the NEBOSH website (www.nebosh.org.uk).

Unit IOG1: Management of International Oil and Gas Health and Safety	
Element 1	Health, Safety and Environmental Management in Context
Element 2	Hydrocarbon Process Safety 1
Element 3	Hydrocarbon Process Safety 2
Element 4	Fire Protection and Emergency Response
Element 5	Logistics and Transport Operations
	Revision and Examination Preparation

Assessment

To complete the qualification you need to pass a formal written exam – Unit IOG1: Management of International Oil and Gas Operational Safety.

This is a two-hour exam, consisting of one long question (20% of the marks) and ten short questions (each being 8% of the total marks). You must answer **all** questions.

To help you prepare, this textbook contains Exam Skills activities at the end of each element of your course. Guidance on how to answer an exam-style question is provided, together with a suggested answer for you to compare to your own.

More Information

As you work your way through this book, always remember to relate your own experiences in the workplace to the topics you study. Appreciation of the practical application and significance of health and safety will help you understand the topics.

Remember, the NEBOSH International Technical Certificate in Oil and Gas Operational Safety is a technical qualification and requires knowledge of the principles of health and safety. NEBOSH has commented that those undertaking the course should have a good understanding of safety issues, which can be from experience or from having studied other NEBOSH Certificate or Diploma level qualifications.

Keeping Yourself Up to Date

The field of health and safety is constantly evolving and, as such, it will be necessary for you to keep up to date with changing legislation and best practice.

RRC publishes updates to all its course materials via a quarterly e-newsletter (issued in February, May, August and November), which alerts students to key changes in legislation, best practice and other information pertinent to current courses. Please visit www.rrc.co.uk/news-resources/newsletters.aspx to access these updates.

User Guide

Before you start to use this textbook, take a moment to read this User Guide.

At the start of each element you will find a Contents table and a list of Learning Outcomes. These are important because they give you an idea of the different topics you will be studying and what you are aiming to achieve.

KEY INFORMATION

Each main section of material starts with a Key Information box. This box presents an overview of the important facts, ideas and principles dealt with under the section heading. There is no depth or detail here, just the basics.

After the Key Information box comes the main content. The main content has been designed to explain and describe the topics specified in the relevant section of the syllabus to the expected level. Wherever possible, the content has been subdivided to give structure. Examples have been given to illustrate various ideas and principles in a variety of different workplaces.

TOPIC FOCUS

Topic Focus boxes contain depth and detail and concentrate on a very specific topic area.

GLOSSARY

Glossary boxes contain descriptions or definitions of words or phrases that are referenced in the main content.

HINTS AND TIPS

Hints and Tips boxes contain simple ideas that can help you as you work through the materials and prepare for the end-of-course exam.

MORE...

More... boxes contain sources of further information. (Websites are current at the time of writing.) Although this book includes everything you need, it is worth looking at these additional sources if you can. This will give you a broader and deeper understanding.

REVISION QUESTIONS

At the end of each section you will find Revision Questions. These are not past exam questions, but should be useful for self-assessment.

You can mark your answers against the suggested answers provided.

EXAM SKILLS

After each element you will find a short Exam Skills section containing an exam-style question (or two) for you to practise answering. Guidance on how to answer is provided, together with a Suggested Answer for you to compare to your own.

Summary

Each element finishes with a Summary. This presents a very concise reflection of the key ideas and principles contained in the element. When you have finished studying an element you might use the summary to test your recall of the detailed information contained within the element.

When you have studied all of the elements in a unit you should move on to look at the Revision and Examination guide.

HEALTH, SAFETY AND ENVIRONMENTAL MANAGEMENT IN CONTEXT

ELEMENT
1

LEARNING OUTCOMES

On completion of this element, you should be able to demonstrate understanding of the content by applying what you have learnt to familiar and unfamiliar situations. In particular, you should be able to:

1 Explain the purpose of and procedures for investigating incidents and how the lessons learnt can be used to improve health and safety in the oil and gas industries.

2 Explain the hazards inherent in oil and gas arising from the extraction, storage, and processing of raw materials and products.

3 Outline the risk management techniques used in the oil and gas industries.

4 Explain the purpose and content of an organisation's documented evidence to provide a convincing and valid argument that a system is adequately safe in the oil and gas industries.

Contents

Learning from Incidents

KEY INFORMATION

- Investigating incidents is important, as is effective root-cause analysis and the recommendation of improvements, in order to make every effort to avoid future incidents.
- Lessons can be learnt from major incidents, especially with regard to management, and from cultural and technical (process) failures that lead to incidents occurring.
- Incidents can take many forms, including near-misses, accidents, dangerous occurrences and ill-health conditions.

INVESTIGATING INCIDENTS

When an incident occurs in the workplace, it should be recorded and investigated. The main reason for this is that, having happened once, it may happen again; and when it happens again the outcome may be as bad as, or worse than, it was the first time. We must therefore attempt to understand exactly why the incident happened so that corrective actions can be taken to prevent a recurrence.

Near-misses are an indicator of potential consequences – what might have been. Often, the only thing that separates a near-miss from an accident is luck – so regard each near-miss as a "free warning".

All incidents and near-misses in the workplace should be recorded and investigated.

All near-misses should be examined to determine the potential for serious harm. Where this potential exists, a thorough investigation should be carried out to prevent that harm from becoming actual. This is not to say that all incidents should be investigated in great depth and detail – that would be a waste of time and effort in many cases – but it is to say that all incidents should be examined for the potential for serious harm so a decision can be made as to whether more detailed investigation is required. This idea is sometimes formalised into an organisation's incident investigation procedure.

The objective of any such investigation is to determine why the organisation's policies and procedures failed. Consequently the incident investigation process is an important part of the health and safety management system. As it is management who ultimately make the decisions and allocate resources, it is vitally important that they are actively involved at every step of the investigation process, including making sure that any recommendations are fully implemented and closed out.

Learning from Incidents

Types of Incident

- **Near-miss** – an unplanned event that had the potential to cause injury, ill health, loss or damage but did not, in fact, do so (a worker was narrowly missed by oil spurting from a burst pipeline).
- **Accident** – an unplanned, unwanted event, which leads to injury, damage or loss.
  - **Injury accident** – where an unplanned, unwanted event leads to some sort of personal injury (e.g. a cut hand).
  - **Damage-only accident** – where the unplanned, unwanted event leads to equipment or property damage, or loss of materials, etc. (e.g. a wall is knocked down by a vehicle).
- **Dangerous occurrence** – a specified event that has been reported to the relevant authority by statute law (e.g. a major gas release).
- **Ill health** – a disease or medical condition that is directly attributable to work (e.g. dermatitis from exposure to oils and greases).

It is important to remember the importance of investigating **all** of the above types of incident, not just those we expect to lead to fatalities, or major injury.

Basic Investigation Procedures

There are some basic principles and procedures that can be used when investigating an incident:

Step 1: Gather factual information about the event.

Step 2: Analyse that information and draw conclusions about the immediate and root causes.

Step 3: Identify suitable corrective measures.

Step 4: Plan the remedial actions.

However, before the investigation can begin there are two important issues that have to be considered:

- **Safety of the scene** – is the area safe to approach? Is immediate action needed to eliminate danger even before casualties are attended to?
- **Casualty care** – any injured people will require first-aid treatment and possibly hospitalisation. This is a priority. The welfare of uninjured bystanders also has to be taken into account – they may be suffering shock.

Once the immediate dangers have been dealt with and casualties attended to, a decision should be made regarding the type and level of investigation that is needed. Should it be:

- A relatively simple investigation of an incident that caused only minor outcomes and did not have the potential for serious outcomes?
- A more in-depth and thorough investigation of an incident with serious outcomes or potential for serious outcomes?

The first type of investigation might be carried out by the line manager of the area; the second type often involves a team of investigators, which might include a safety specialist, senior managers, a technical specialist and perhaps a worker representative.

Offshore investigating teams may also include installation specialists from services such as drilling, well services, maintenance, process, and deck crews. In the most serious or major cases, an inspector from the national safety enforcing agency (for example, the Health and Safety Executive in the UK may become involved and conduct or lead an investigation.

STEP 1: GATHERING INFORMATION

- Secure the scene as soon as possible to prevent it being altered.
- Collect witnesses' details quickly, before they start to move away. In some cases, it may help to remove witnesses from the scene and ask them to wait in a separate area. If there are many witnesses it may be better to separate them from each other to prevent collusion or contamination of their testimony.
- Collect factual information from the scene and record it. This might be done by means of:
  - Photographs.
  - Sketches.
  - Measurements.
  - Videos.
  - Written descriptions of factors such as wind speed, temperature, etc.
  - Taking physical evidence.

  The investigator should come prepared with the appropriate equipment to record this information.
- Once the scene has been thoroughly examined, move on to the second source of information: witnesses.

  Witnesses often provide crucial evidence about what occurred before, during and after incidents. They should be interviewed carefully to make sure that good-quality evidence is gathered.

The investigator should collect factual information from the scene and record it

- Once witnesses have been interviewed, move on to the third source of information: documentation. Various documents may be examined during an incident investigation, such as:
  - Company policy.
  - Risk assessments.
  - Training records.
  - Safe systems of work.
  - Permits-to-work.
  - Maintenance records.
  - Disciplinary records.
  - Internal accident report forms.
  - Log-book entries.
  - Computer printouts relevant to the situation.

TOPIC FOCUS

Good witness-interview technique requires that the interviewer should:

- Hold the interview in a quiet room or area free from distractions and interruptions.
- Introduce themselves and try to establish rapport with the witness using appropriate verbal and body language.
- Explain the purpose of the interview (perhaps emphasising that the interview is not about blaming people).
- Use open questions, such as those beginning with What? Why? Where? When? Who? How? etc. that do not put words into the witnesses' mouths and do not allow them to answer with a "yes" or "no".
- Keep an open mind.
- Take notes so that the facts being discussed are not forgotten.
- Ask the witness to write and sign a statement to create a record of their testimony. Thank the witness for their help.

Learning from Incidents

STEP 2: ANALYSING INFORMATION

The purpose here is to draw conclusions about the immediate and root causes of the incident.

Immediate causes are the obvious causes that gave rise to the event itself. These will be the things that occurred at the time and place of the accident. For example, a worker slips on a patch of oil spilt on the floor, injuring his back as he falls backwards and hits the ground. The immediate cause of the back injury is hitting the ground, but there are many contributors to this cause. It is common to think of these in terms of unsafe acts and unsafe conditions. So here, for example, we might have the slippery oil (unsafe condition), and the worker walking through it (unsafe act).

Underlying or root causes are the things that lie behind the immediate causes. Often, root causes will be failures in the management system, such as:

- Failure to adequately supervise workers.
- Failure to provide appropriate PPE.
- Failure to provide adequate training.
- Lack of maintenance.
- Inadequate checking or inspections.
- Failure to carry out proper risk assessments.

Accidents that happen in workplaces usually have at least one immediate cause and one underlying or root cause, often more. The root cause gives rise to the immediate cause, which, in turn, gives rise to the accident (rather like a row of dominoes falling; in fact, this idea is often referred to as the **Domino Theory** of accident causation).

If that one root cause is identified and dealt with, then the accident should not happen again. For example, if a worker twists their ankle in a pothole in the pavement then the obvious solution is to fill the pothole in. That deals with the immediate cause. It would also be worth asking how long the pothole had been there. If it had been there for a long time, why was it not spotted sooner? And if it had been spotted, why had it been left unrepaired with no interim measure being taken to protect people?

These questions might identify an underlying cause such as inadequate inspection and maintenance, or failure to put interim measures in place while waiting for maintenance work to be carried out. Any such root cause needs to be dealt with if similar accidents are to be prevented in future.

In contrast to this single-cause idea, some workplace accidents are complex and have multiple causes: there are several immediate causes for the accident and each of these has one or more underlying or root cause. This idea is usually referred to as **Multi-Causation Theory**.

EXAMPLE 1 (ONSHORE)

A WORKER MIGHT BE STRUCK BY A LOAD BEING CARRIED BY A FORKLIFT TRUCK.

Immediate causes for such an accident might be:

- Failure to secure the load on the pallet.
- Poor road positioning of the truck close to a pedestrian exit.
- Aggressive braking by the truck driver.
- An inattentive pedestrian stepping out in front of the truck.

On investigation, each of these immediate causes might have their own separate **root causes**, such as:

- No training for the driver, who is new to the workplace, has not worked with this type of load before and is unaware of the load-securing technique required.
- Lack of segregation of pedestrian and traffic routes; no barriers and no markings to separate the two.
- Lack of proper driver induction into their new workplace, so they are unaware of the layout and position of pedestrian exits, etc.
- Poor maintenance of the truck.
- No refresher training for existing staff, meaning that experienced staff have become complacent.

If there are multiple causes for the accident then it is important that each of these causes is identified during the investigation; otherwise, incomplete remedial action will be taken and similar accidents may happen in the future.

EXAMPLE 2 (ONSHORE/OFFSHORE)

A WORKER SLIPS ON A PATCH OF SPILT OIL.

Immediate causes:

- The slip hazard (unsafe condition).
- The worker walking through the oil (unsafe act).

With such a slip, the root causes might be a poorly maintained machine that has leaked oil onto the floor, and a poorly inspected and maintained workshop (where the oil leak was) with broken light fittings and inadequate lighting levels. Here, the worker might be blameless on the basis that, given those conditions, the incident was bound to happen eventually.

EXAMPLE 3 (OFFSHORE)

A LIFTING SLING BREAKS ON THE DRILLING DECK.

Immediate causes:

- A damaged and worn sling (unsafe condition).
- A worker using the sling in poor condition (unsafe act).

With this offshore scenario, the **root causes** again fall to poorly maintained equipment, with a less than adequate inspection and sling replacement system, together, perhaps, with inadequate storage of lifting equipment, possibly exposing it to a harsh environment, being dropped on the deck, not hung up, etc. In this case, there is some responsibility on the worker not to use a sling that is in poor condition. The fact that they did use it could be a result of lack of training in care and use of lifting equipment.

Consequences could have been many, including dropping equipment over the side into the sea, striking a worker (or workers) on the drilling rig beneath the sling, damage to plant on the drilling deck, etc.

STEP 3: IDENTIFY SUITABLE CONTROL MEASURES

Once the immediate and underlying causes of the accident are known, appropriate control measures can be identified. It is important that the correct control measures are established, otherwise time, money and effort will be wasted on inadequate and unnecessary measures that will not prevent similar occurrences in the future.

Control measures must be identified to remedy both the immediate and underlying causes. Immediate causes are usually easy to identify – if there is a spill of oil on the floor, clean it up; if the guard is missing from the machine, reattach it.

Underlying causes can be harder to determine because they reflect failure of the management system, but it is essential that the correct control measures to remedy the failure of the management system are identified because this will help prevent similar accidents occurring in similar circumstances across the entire organisation:

- Clean up the oil leaking out of the vehicle in the distribution depot but fail to deal with the underlying cause (lack of inspection and maintenance) and more leaks will occur which, in turn, will lead to more pedestrian slips (and perhaps, more alarming, vehicle skids).
- Clean up the oil leaking out of the vehicle and deal with the underlying cause (by introducing a proper inspection and maintenance system) and there is a good chance that most oil leaks will be prevented in the future for all vehicles in the fleet at all locations.

Perhaps the most important questions to ask when identifying control measures are:

- If this action is taken, will it prevent this same accident from happening in exactly the same way at this location?
- If this action is taken, will it prevent other similar types of accident from happening in similar locations in the future?

If the answer to both of these questions is "no", then you need to identify other control measures.

Learning from Incidents

STEP 4: PLAN THE REMEDIAL ACTIONS

An accident investigation should lead to corrective action being taken, in just the same way as a workplace inspection will.

Remedial actions can be presented in an action plan:

Recommended action	Priority	Timescale	Responsible person
Introduce induction training for all new drivers	Medium	1 month	Warehouse manager
Introduce new inspection and maintenance system	High	1 week	Maintenance manager

When the action plan is being prepared, appropriate immediate and interim control measures must be given suitable priorities and timescales. Unsafe conditions must not be allowed to persist in the workplace. Dangerous practices and high-risk activities must be dealt with immediately. This means that immediate action must be taken to remedy such circumstances when they are discovered. Machinery and equipment may have to be taken out of action, certain work activities suspended, and locations evacuated. These responses cannot be left until the investigation has been completed. They will have to be implemented immediately to ensure safety while the investigation is in progress.

There may be interim control measures that can be introduced in the short to medium term to allow work to proceed while longer-term solutions are pending. For example:

- Hearing protection might be introduced as a short-term control measure until the maintenance of a piece of machinery that is producing excessive noise has been completed.
- A perimeter guard might be fitted around an overheating machine that would ordinarily be protected with a fixed enclosed guard while new cooling units are sourced and delivered.

Underlying causes will often demand significant time, money and effort to remedy. It is essential, therefore, that the remedial actions that will have the greatest impact are prioritised and timetabled first. There may be actions that have to be taken (to address a management weakness, or to achieve legal compliance) that will not be as effective in preventing future accidents. These actions should still be taken, but with a lower priority.

COST OF REMEDIAL ACTIONS

It is worth bearing in mind that there is always an element of cost involved when taking remedial action. Remember that there will not only be immediate costs, but also ongoing costs.

An example of this would be the simple matter of providing personal protective equipment. If a task required respiratory protection to be worn, in the form of half-masks with replaceable filters, the initial cost would be for the masks and filters themselves, face-fit tests for users of the masks, storage facilities such as boxes, cases or cupboards, and the ongoing requirements for regular formal inspections of the masks by the users. Also ongoing would be the cost of replacing the filters and, eventually, the masks.

Where slings were not being cared for on an offshore installation, the remedial costs could be a supply of new slings, training for all users of lifting equipment, the introduction of a formal inspection, examination and testing programme, and new storage facilities away from harsh conditions. Ongoing costs would be regular supervision, maintenance of the storage facility, the regular inspection, examination and testing programme and occasional replacement of slings.

IMPORTANCE OF LEARNING FROM MAJOR INCIDENTS

It is vital that lessons are learned from all major incidents, as management, cultural and technical failures (i.e. process failures) must be understood so that incidents can be prevented from happening again.

There is much to be learned from investigations carried out into internal incidents, but the outcomes of other incidents also provide important information. An old saying in health and safety is: "There is no such thing as an accident – only a management failure." But remember that this statement is not laying the blame for incidents on managers. Instead, it suggests that health and safety was **managed** poorly overall by having inadequate safety systems in place.

For instance, an action as simple as misplacing a permit-to-work certificate was just one of the root causes of the Piper Alpha incident in the North Sea. There are other parallels that can be drawn from Piper Alpha, too, in management, cultural and technical failures that contributed to the loss of the oil rig and 167 lives.

The Piper Alpha Disaster

On the morning of 6 July 1988, as part of a maintenance programme, a gas-pump pressure safety valve was removed from the processing area and, as the work could not be completed that day, a blanking plate was fitted over the end of the pipe where the pump had been removed. That evening, another pump failed. Without the engineers knowing (possibly owing to the loss of a permit-to-work certificate) the safety valve was still off the process, and when they tried to start it the escaping gas exploded, penetrating the firewalls. Gas and oil pipes suffered in the heat and provided further fuel to the growing fire.

Although there was an automatic deluge sprinkler system in place, which could pump hundreds of tons of sea water onto a fire, it was switched off because divers had been in the water, and it could only operate manually. It was not switched back on to automatic, and when it was needed it did not operate.

Twenty minutes after the initial explosion, large-diameter gas pipes (up to 900mm) weakened and burst, releasing gas at two thousand pounds per square-inch pressure, increasing the size of the fire.

A rescue boat arrived, but could not deploy its equipment quickly as it shut down when turned on, so this did not provide assistance quickly enough.

Many workers took refuge in the accommodation block but the coming and going and opening of doors allowed smoke in. The accommodation block was not smoke-proofed. By this time no one could get to the lifeboats, so many workers went to the extremities of the rig and jumped into the sea. Sixty-two people survived by taking this action. The accommodation block slipped into the sea, and a major part of the platform followed it.

The other 167 people on the rig lost their lives in the disaster. The whole incident occurred in just 22 minutes, the after-effects continuing into the night

MORE...

You can find out more about the Piper Alpha disaster by referring to:

The Public Enquiry into the Piper Alpha Disaster, Cullen, The Honourable Lord, The Stationery Office, 1990, ISBN 9780101131025

A LESSON LEARNED

This incident was instrumental in bringing about the introduction of the **Offshore Installations (Safety Case) Regulations 2005** in the UK (see later), and the regulatory control of offshore installations was taken over by the Health and Safety Executive (HSE) in 1991.

Some of the problems highlighted and lessons learned from the Piper Alpha disaster include:

- **Permit-to-Work Systems** – (paperwork systems used in high risk situations to control activities by closely monitoring the work carried out). The Piper Alpha systems had been relaxed, allowing less formal systems to operate, particularly relating to control of permits and communication at the shift hand-over. Proper adherence to the formal system and close control at the shift hand-over would have retained the hand-over permit and prevented the pump without the safety valve ever being started, so averting the disaster.

  Following Piper Alpha, the introduction of a permit co-ordinator and facilities for permitry were instigated. Control-room competencies were also subject to review.

- **Safety Management** – vital in any industry, but more so in high-risk industries such as this, it was shown (in Lord Cullen's report on the disaster) to be lacking. It was described as "superficial". Not all managers had adequate qualifications, and they tolerated poor practices and did not appear to audit systems properly. The delays in decision-making allowed oil production to continue from other connected platforms while the fire raged on Piper Alpha.

- **Design** – when the original oil exploration rig was adapted for gas processing, no changes were made to the firewalls. The original ones were capable of withstanding fire, but were not built to withstand an explosion, and they were breached in the gas explosions.

  Closely tied in with design was the number and size of pipelines on and attached to the platform, which helped feed the fire.

- **Maintenance Systems** – closely associated with the permit-to-work system:
  - Proper maintenance procedures would have prevented the pump being started without the safety valve.
  - Closer control of the deluge system would have controlled its switching off while divers were in the water, and switching on when the area was clear.
  - Closer attention to audit and inspection reports would have meant that corroded sprinkler pipes and heads were repaired or replaced.

Learning from Incidents

- **Safety Training** – some workers who ignored what they were taught survived by not entering the accommodation block, which eventually failed and sank into the sea. But, in general, training in emergency procedures on and off the platform was lacking. In particular, management leadership was especially inadequate in dealing with such emergencies.
- **Safety Audits** – as in all areas of offshore operations, audits are many and complex. The audits in Occidental Petroleum's North Sea field were in place and carried out on a regular basis, but they were not carried out satisfactorily. They identified few problems, possibly even overlooking issues such as corroding sprinkler deluge pipework. Some issues highlighted in audits were just ignored.

In the UK HSE publication HSG48, *Reducing Error and Influencing Behaviour*, the human contribution and other causes of the Piper Alpha disaster are summarised as:

"Formal inquiry found a number of technical and organisational failures. Maintenance error that eventually led to the leak was the result of inexperience, poor maintenance procedures and poor learning by the organisation. There was a breakdown in communications and the permit-to-work system at shift changeover and safety procedures were not practised sufficiently."

Source: HSG48 Reducing Error and Influencing Behaviour (2nd ed.), HSE, 1999
(www.hse.gov.uk/pubns/books/hsg48.htm)

Toxic Gas Release, Bhopal, December 1984

The Bhopal incident changed the way that the chemical industry organises and manages the storage of chemical stocks, safety standards and safety procedures.

On 3/4 December 1984 a chemical release occurred at the Union Carbide India Ltd. plant in Bhopal, India, causing a massive toxic gas cloud. The process at the plant involved using methyl isocyanate (MIC), an extremely toxic chemical, to make Sevin, a pesticide. About 1,700 to 2,700 (possibly more) people were killed, 50,000 people were seriously affected, and 1,000,000 people were affected in some way by the chemical release. It was one of the worst industrial accidents in history.

The accident occurred when about 120 to 240 gallons of water were allowed to contaminate an MIC storage tank. The MIC hydrolysed, causing heat and pressure, which, in turn, caused the tank rupture disc to burst.

Equipment designed to handle an MIC release included a recirculating caustic soda scrubber tower and a flare system designed to moderate flows from process vents, but not to handle runaway reactions from storage. The design was based on the assumption that full cooling would be provided by the refrigeration system; at the time of the release the refrigeration had been turned off and the flare tower was shut down for repairs. A system of pressurised sprinklers that was supposed to form a water curtain over the escaping gas was deficient, as water pressure was too low for water to reach the height of the escaping gas.

CAUSES OF THE ACCIDENT

There were conflicting stories of how water got into the tank, including operator error, contamination and even sabotage.

The root cause of the accident appeared to be a management system that did not respond adequately to the potential hazards of MIC. There was probably a greater inventory of MIC than was needed. The main process expertise was in the United States and local management did not appear to have understood the process or the consequences of changes made, including plant design, maintenance and operations, back-up systems and community responsibility.

Buncefield, December 2005

The incident at Buncefield oil storage depot at Hemel Hempstead, Hertfordshire, England, happened during the night of 11 December 2005. A major fire occurred, caused by a series of explosions. At least one of the initial explosions was of massive proportions and fire engulfed a large proportion of the site. More than 40 people were injured but there were no fatalities. Significant damage occurred to both commercial and residential properties in the vicinity, and a large area around the site was evacuated on the advice of the emergency services. The fire burned for several days, destroying most of the site and emitting large clouds of black smoke into the atmosphere.

The cause of the incident was the formation of a flammable mixture of petrol (gasoline) or similar spirit, and air that ignited, leading to the explosion and fire.

The filling of a tank (912) with petrol proceeded, and between 19.00 and 03.00 the tank became full and started to overflow. Evidence suggests that the protection system, which should have automatically closed valves to prevent any more filling did not operate. From 05.20 pumping continued, causing fuel to cascade down the sides of the tank and through the air, leading to the rapid formation of a rich fuel/air mixture around the tank.

At 05.38 CCTV footage showed a vapour cloud of around 1m deep, which had increased to 2m deep by 05.46. By 05.50 the vapour cloud began flowing off site, and at 06.01 the first explosion occurred, followed by further explosions and a large fire that engulfed more than 20 large storage tanks. The ignition point might have been a generator house and pump house in the vicinity.

Evidence suggests that a high-level switch, which should have detected that the tank was full and shut off the supply, failed to operate. The switch failure should have triggered an alarm, but that, too, appears to have failed.

The UK Health Protection Agency and Major Incident Investigation Board provided advice to prevent incidents such as this in the future. The primary need was for safety measures to be in place to prevent fuel from exiting the tanks in which it is stored. Added safety measures were needed for when fuel does escape, mainly to prevent it forming a flammable vapour and to stop pollutants poisoning the environment.

Deepwater Horizon Oil Spill, 2010

The Deepwater Horizon oil spill in the Gulf of Mexico near the Mississippi River Delta in the United States of America shows that lessons take some time to learn.

The Deepwater Horizon was a nine-year-old semi-submersible mobile offshore drilling platform, built by Hyundai Heavy Industries of Korea, owned by Transocean and operated under lease by British Petroleum (BP) from March 2008 (to September 2013).

In April 2010, drilling was in progress on an exploratory well at a water depth of approximately 5,000 feet (1,500m) in the Macondo Prospect in the Mississippi Canyon Block, about 41 miles off the Louisiana coast. The installation of production casing was under way, and when completed the well would have been tested for integrity and a cement plug put in place, reserving the well for future use.

On 20 April, high-pressure methane from the well escaped all the way up the drill column and expanded over the platform, igniting and causing an explosion, engulfing the platform in fire. The majority of workers from the platform escaped in lifeboats, but 11 were never found and are presumed to have been killed in the explosion (there were two later oil-related deaths, too).

The platform burned for around 36 hours, and then sank on 22 April. The oil leak was discovered later that day, when a floating oil slick spread where the rig had stood.

On 15 July the wellhead was capped, but not until it had released about 4.9 million barrels (205 million gallons) of crude oil. On 19 September the wellhead was finally sealed off. It has been estimated that around 53,000 barrels a day were escaping just before the wellhead was capped. The US Government announced that it was the 'worst environmental disaster the US has faced'.

The toxicity of the petroleum, oxygen depletion and the oil dispersant Corexit that was used at the location are thought to be the major causes of environmental damage.

Later investigations and witness testimony suggested that in a number of cases leading to the events of 20 April, BP appeared to have chosen riskier procedures, possibly in order to save both time and money, and sometimes against the advice given by their own workers and contractors on the project. The cementing procedure was questioned, and it was suggested that the blowout preventer failed to fully engage, and there may have been problems with both the hydraulics and the controls. Another issue was that protective drilling mud was displaced with seawater just hours before the explosion occurred.

Learning from Incidents

In the US Government Commission findings BP was accused of being responsible for nine faults, including:

- Failure to use a diagnostic tool to test the strength of the cement.
- Ignoring the pressure test that had failed.
- Not plugging the pipe with cement.

(BP was not directly blamed for any of these events.)

The Commission's findings were that what was missing, and therefore needed, were:

- Better management of decision-making processes.
- Better communication between the company and its contractors.
- Effective training of key engineering and rig personnel.

Safety Culture

All groups of people (such as factory-workers, office staff, the crew of a ship or the workforce on an oil rig) develop a "safety culture".

An organisation with a good health and safety culture will have high regard for health and safety, and good perception of risk will be shared by all involved, with workers adopting the same positive attitudes – that health and safety is their problem and they will deal with it appropriately.

This positive culture will therefore influence how all individuals in the workforce handle new events (such as emergencies) and make decisions during those events. The workforce will not put operational requirements before health and safety. A good safety culture requires effective safety management systems and management commitment.

The failures identified in the Piper Alpha disaster included faults in organisational structures and procedures (culture) and identified them as equally important contributory factors as the individual human and technical failures.

MORE...

UK HSE information on hydrocarbon releases currently indicates a continuing decline in major and minor releases:

http://www.hse.gov.uk/press/2012/hse-offshorestats1112.htm?ebul=hsegen&cr=9/6-aug-12.

A copy of the HSE Offshore Safety Statistics Bulletin 2011/12 is available at:

http://www.hse.gov.uk/offshore/statistics/stat1112.pdf.

GLOSSARY

SAFETY CULTURE
A system of shared values and beliefs about the importance of health and safety in the workplace, and the associated way of behaving.

REVISION QUESTIONS

1. Why are accident investigations carried out?
2. What are the four steps in the investigation process?
3. Identify the categories of staff who might be considered useful members of an internal accident investigation team.
4. List the types of documentation that might be consulted during an accident investigation.
5. What are the two categories of immediate cause of accidents/incidents?
6. A worker has been hit by a reversing vehicle in a loading bay. List possible immediate causes and root causes.

(Suggested Answers are at the end.)

Hazards Inherent in Oil and Gas

TERMINOLOGY

GLOSSARY

- **Flash point** – the lowest temperature at which there is sufficient vaporisation of a substance capable of producing a flash momentarily when a source of ignition is applied.

- **Vapour density** (mass of vapour per unit volume) or **relative vapour density** (density of the vapour relative to air) – indicates whether a flammable vapour is likely to rise in the air, or, more commonly, sink and accumulate in low-lying areas.

- **Vapour pressure** – the pressure exerted by a vapour when the liquid and vapour are in equilibrium (such as in a closed vessel).

  It increases with temperature and a high vapour pressure at a given temperature means that the liquid is very volatile and more likely to produce a flammable vapour.

- **Flammable limits** (also known as explosive limits when applied to explosions):
  - **Lower flammable limit** (LFL) or **lower explosive limit** (LEL): the minimum concentration of fuel in air that is sufficient to allow combustion to occur. Below the LFL, the mixture is too lean to burn.
  - **Upper flammable limit** (UFL) or **upper explosive limit** (UEL): the maximum concentration of fuel in air that is sufficient to allow combustion to occur. Above the UFL the mixture is too rich to burn.

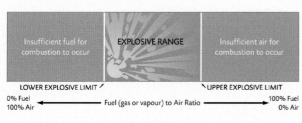

Flammable limits

- **Flammable, highly flammable and extremely flammable:**
  - **Flammable liquid** – liquids with a flash point 21-55°C (inclusive) (i.e. around ambient temperature).
  - **Highly flammable** – liquids with a flash point less than 21°C (i.e. below ambient temperature), but which are not extremely flammable and certain reactive substances.
  - **Extremely flammable** – liquids with a flash point below 0°C and a boiling point less than or equal to 35°C (i.e. very low flash point and low boiling point, therefore high volatility).

The upper and lower flammable limits are expressed in units of volume per cent. Between these limits is the flammable (or explosive) range.

Gas detectors are used to control the hazard of fires and explosions and are set at a level below the lower explosive limit (LEL) to ensure that a flammable mixture does not exist anywhere in the area being monitored by the sensor (normally at, or under 10% of the LEL).

- **Very toxic** – produces serious, acute or chronic ill health, or death at very small doses.

- **Toxic** – produces serious, acute or chronic ill health, or death at very small or small doses.

- **Harmful** – produces serious, acute or chronic ill health, or death at larger doses.

- **Corrosive** – destroys living tissue by direct chemical attack.

- **Irritant** – causes inflammation, in particular of the mucous membranes.

- **Sensitising** – can cause an allergic response following either single acute overexposure or repeated chronic overexposures.

- **Carcinogenic** – can induce the growth of malignant tumours. Malignant tumours are cancer tumours capable of causing serious ill health or death.

Hazards Inherent in Oil and Gas

PROPERTIES AND HAZARDS OF GASES

Gases are used and created in the production and processing of oil and gas, so we must look at the properties of gases and the hazards associated with them.

- **Hydrogen** – widely used in petroleum refining as a catalyst regenerator, it is a highly flammable and explosive gas, which forms ignitable mixtures in air over a very wide range of concentrations (between 4.9% and 75%). It is colourless and odourless and very light, and explosive mixtures form rapidly. It can be easily ignited by low-energy sparks. It is not a toxic gas, but can asphyxiate at high concentrations. It can react vigorously with oxidising agents.

- **Methane** – also known as marsh gas and fire damp, it is used in the manufacture of hydrocarbons and is the main fuel constituent of natural gas. It is highly flammable and explosive, and forms an ignitable mixture with air over a wide range of concentrations (5% – 15%). Again, it is very light and may collect beneath structures such as roofs, ceilings and platforms, creating pockets of explosive mixtures. Methane is a simple asphyxiant, and an odorising agent is usually added to it.

- **Liquefied Petroleum Gas (LPG) (Propane/Butane)** – gas at normal temperature and pressure, but readily liquefied under pressure. It is a feedstock for chemical petroleum manufacture, as well as a fuel gas for heating, cooking, lighting, and the operation of internal combustion engines. It is also used as a fuel gas in welding and cutting, and in the manufacture of high-octane liquid fuels. LPG is highly flammable and, being denser than air, it collects at low level and readily forms an explosive mixture. In some cases, weak concentrations can be ignited with the flame readily flashing back to the source of a leak. Inhalation can lead to drowsiness, and exposure to moderately high concentrations can prove serious. It is colourless and odourless, and has an odorising agent added except where used in a chemical reaction. It is an asphyxiant.

  The dangers of LPG lie with its flammability and explosive properties, and the fact that it is stored under great pressure, and hence very low temperatures, to retain its liquid state. On release, LPG reverts to its gaseous state, with rapid and considerable increase in volume.

  While the main risks are from fire and explosion, the fact that the gas is heavier than air is of significance to persons working in low-lying or confined areas (such as excavations, pits, etc.) because of its asphyxiating properties. For persons handling cylinders, pipework and connections for LPG systems there is a risk of frost burns due to the low temperatures, and cylinders pose a manual-handling risk.

- **Liquefied Natural Gas (LNG)** – as the name suggests, a liquefied methane (North Sea gas has 93.7% methane) used as a fuel gas for heating, cooking, etc. From the liquefied state it easily vaporises, forming a highly-flammable odourless gas, again having an odorising agent added. It will form an explosive mixture with air. Vapour can be ignited some distance away from a leak and the flame will spread back to the source. It is a simple asphyxiant, and non-toxic as a gas.

  Contact with its liquefied form will cause frostbite; LNG is cold (boiling at -161°C). On release, LNG reverts to its gaseous state, with rapid and considerable increase in volume. It is usually stored as a liquid at atmospheric pressure in special steel inner tanks with outer concrete shells with no bottom connections.

  Pressurised storage and transport is not used, reducing the dangers of catastrophic vessel failure with results such as boiling liquid expanding vapour explosions (BLEVEs). The unintentional release of LNG and its dispersion will create fire and explosion hazards such as pool fire spread, evaporation and pool fires.

- **Nitrogen** – a common odourless, colourless gas, tasteless and non-flammable, making up naturally 78% of the Earth's atmosphere. Industrial nitrogen is produced by the fractional distillation of air. In industry it is commonly used to "inert" flammable atmospheres, as a "cover" on flammable and explosive substances (a gas layer lying above the liquid in a tank) and to inflate tyres, used in a form often called OFN – oxygen-free nitrogen.

  In addition to inerting and cover capabilities, liquefied nitrogen is used for pipe freezing and pipeline purging. Offshore it is used for a number of well services operations, such as drill stem testing or perforating operations, nitrogen lift, etc.

- **Hydrogen Sulphide** – a colourless flammable gas with an offensive odour of rotten eggs, which forms explosive mixtures with air over a wide range of concentrations (4% – 46%). It is denser than air and will accumulate in low-level areas, and can travel long distances to an ignition source and flash back. Hydrogen sulphide is toxic, and will irritate the eyes, skin and respiratory tract and can lead to respiratory paralysis. It will rapidly deaden the sense of smell, so its odour cannot be relied on to detect it. It often occurs in natural areas, such as swamps, ponds and lagoons and where there is rotting vegetable matter.

  The effects of hydrogen sulphide depend on duration of exposure, frequency of exposure and the intensity (concentration of the gas), as well as the susceptibility of the person exposed.

Since it is present in some subsurface formations, drilling and other operational crews must be prepared to use detection equipment, personal protective equipment (particularly respiratory protective equipment) and require adequate training backed up by contingency procedures in case of overexposure in hydrogen sulphide-prone areas. It will enter drilling mud from subsurface formations, can be generated by sulphate-reducing bacteria in stored muds, and formed in concrete leg platforms below the gas-tight floor.

- **Oxygen** – a colourless, odourless gas that is essential to support combustion. Oxygen enrichment can lead to fires and explosion, and will react violently with oils and greases. It is used with fuel gases in welding and burning to intensify combustion.

  Oxygen is non-flammable, but will encourage combustion, combustible materials becoming more easily ignited in an oxygen-enriched atmosphere. They burn far more rapidly with near explosive violence, as illustrated by the fire that broke out on HMS Glasgow, Newcastle upon Tyne, UK, below decks in an atmosphere enriched by leaking oxygen cylinders. The fierce, rapid fire caused the death of eight workers on the ship and others, including fire-fighters, were overcome by smoke and needed hospital treatment.

  Oxygen can easily be absorbed into clothing and under these conditions a simple spark or other small source of ignition can result in flash-burning. Oxygen is sometimes used offshore to detect and quantify the flow of water in or around a borehole based on oxygen activation.

MORE...

Guidance on the hazards from using oxygen in the workplace and the precautions needed when using oxygen equipment are set out in the UK HSE's INDG459 Oxygen Use in the Workplace: Fire and Explosion Hazards, available at:

http://www.hse.gov.uk/pubns/indg459.pdf

PROPERTIES AND HAZARDS OF ASSOCIATED PRODUCTS AND CONTROL MEASURES

PROPERTIES

- **Anti-foaming agents** (defoamers) are used in process and cooling liquids to reduce problems caused by foam and dissolved or trapped air, such as:
    - Cavitation reducing pump efficiency (and creating noise).
    - Reduction in the capacity of pumps and storage tanks.
    - Bacterial growth in the fluids.
    - Dirt and debris formation and surface flotation.

  Anti-foam agents come in many chemical bases such as oil, powder, water, silicone and glycol.

- **Anti-wetting agents** – generally, coatings intended to place a waterproof barrier between the surface of a material (usually metal and wood) and water, such as the sea and wet weather. Anti-wetting agents in this respect provide good anti-corrosive protection.

- **Micro-biocides** – anti-bacterial treatments added to industrial fluids, usually cooling and process water, especially in standing supplies such as ponds, lagoons, reservoirs, etc, and static water-storage facilities.

- **Corrosion preventatives** – additives for industrial fluids to delay or prevent the formation of corrosion within fuel systems and process pipelines.

- **Refrigerants** – substances used in a heat cycle usually including a phase-change from a gas to a liquid. Propane is a common refrigerant, as CFCs are being replaced. Other applications may use ammonia, sulphur dioxide and methane.

Hazards Inherent in Oil and Gas

HAZARDS AND RISK CONTROLS

- **Hazards**

  The hazards of these products are related to the:

  - Physical form (powder, liquid, vapour, gas), which determines the potential route of entry into the body (inhalation, ingestion, skin absorption or penetration).
  - Hazard classification (toxic, harmful, irritant, corrosive, sensitising, carcinogenic).

- **Control Measures**

  - Risk assessment for use of hazardous substances.
  - Automated dosing systems instead of hand-dosing.
  - Safe storage and handling procedures.
  - PPE suitable for the nature and extent of the hazard (e.g. waterproof/chemical-resistant clothing, goggles, respiratory protective equipment).

ASSOCIATED PRODUCTS

- **Water and steam** – used extensively in processes such as system cooling, lubrication (drilling muds) and sea water for fire deluge.

  Water flooding and steam flooding are frequently used as advanced recovery methods to increase reservoir pressure to "push" hydrocarbons out. This usually requires the use of injection wells and is often pressure or high oil viscosity. This can increase the amount of oil ultimately recoverable.

  A method of thermal recovery is often used in which a well is injected with steam, which is then put back in production. Cyclic steam injection is used extensively in heavy-oil reservoirs, tar sands, and, in some cases, to improve injectivity before steam flood, or in-situ combustion operations. Steam is used in re-boilers onshore.

  Steam is a good reservoir for heat energy and heat transfer, which is one of its industrial uses. However, if steam comes into contact with persons there is a serious risk of scalding. Steam generated from a volume of water occupies over 1000 times this volume and this expansion process drives pistons or turbines in a steam engine. However the pressure generated from this expansion has also been the cause of many boiler explosions in the past and, consequently, steam boilers require a range of protective devices to prevent over-pressurisation. Condensation of steam causes a reduction in volume and can produce a vacuum great enough to collapse a vessel.

  - **Hazards** associated with high-pressure and high-temperature water and steam are pressure injection of fluids into the body, as well as severe steam burns. Exposure to inhalation of high concentrations of steam can cause burning in the lungs and even asphyxiation.
  - **Safe handling** procedures must be in place, together with the use of appropriate water and heat-proof clothing to resist steam burns.

You will find more on the use of furnaces and boilers to heat water to produce steam in Element 3.

- **Mercaptans** – a group of sulphur-containing organic chemical substances, with offensive odours, like rotting cabbage, which make them very noticeable in the air. They are sometimes used as an odorising agent in natural gas to make it detectable.

  Processes are in place in oil refineries and natural gas-processing plants that remove hydrogen sulphide and mercaptans – known as "sweeteners", they remove the sour, foul odours.

  Leaks or discharges of mercaptans are easily detected by smell. They can lead to headaches and nausea when inhaled, accompanied by vomiting. Coughing, irritation of the lungs and inflammation of the eyes may result. Very high concentrations may lead to breathing difficulties and cyanosis (turning blue), loss of consciousness and muscle spasms. Appropriate respiratory protective equipment (RPE) should be worn where potentially harmful levels may be present.

- **Drilling muds** (also known as drilling fluids) – are used in drilling deep holes, as in oil and gas extraction. The mud is often an integral part of the process, serving a number of functions, but particularly as a lubricant. Drilling muds cut down the friction experienced, lower the heat and reduce the chances of friction-related complications. The mud also acts as a carrier for the materials through which drilling takes place, suspending it and carrying it up to the surface. Different muds will be used in different circumstances, based on their viscosity and density. Muds can be aqueous (water-based, non-aqueous (gas-based), and may contain minerals, or be totally synthetic in nature.

  - **Hazards** associated with drilling muds include contact with the additives (e.g. diesel oil and its fumes, anti-foaming agents) and the natural gases and flammable materials that can be returned to the drilling work areas, leading to a fire or explosion risk, especially around shale shaker/conveyor areas, before being returned to the mud pits.
  - **Suitable controls** will include fire safety precautions, and appropriate PPE to prevent unnecessary skin contact with the muds.

- **Sludges** (drilling wastes) – including low specific activity (LSA) sludges. Depending on the nature of the base (the geological formation) being drilled for oil and gas, there may be naturally-occurring radionuclides, such as uranium and thorium (referred to as NORM – Naturally Occurring Radioactive Materials). LSA sludges are routinely found in both onshore and offshore activities.

They will be contained in the brine solution (formation water) that is around the pockets of oil and gas, and will be contained within the drilling content and returned to the surface.

The radioactive decay products (usually radium) can stay in solution, or settle out to form sludges in tanks and mud pits, or form mineral scale inside pipelines and drilling components. In gas production areas, LSA can be in the form of lead-scale. Pyrophoric iron is often found in sludges offshore and onshore and needs special control measures for its disposal because of its properties.

In oil and gas production, LSA scale is typically found in:

- The production well.
- Safety valves.
- Wellheads.
- Production manifolds.
- Separators.
- Water separators.

The activity of LSA scale depends on how much radium is present, and the content of radium will vary with the type of rock and its content of uranium and thorium. LSA scale is not easily soluble, and its removal from production equipment requires the use of specialist dispersal chemicals, or high-pressure water-flushing.

The risk to workers will depend on the activity of the material, and arises from possible:

- Inhalation of radioactive dust from dried contamination.
- Direct contact with radioactive sludge.
- Ingestion of radioactive contamination.

It is important that all personnel working with LSA scale protect themselves and others from contact with radioactive materials.

LSA sludges vary from standard sludge, through soft, easily removed scales, to very hard and tenacious scales, and the levels of radioactivity will vary from just above "background" to levels requiring restricted, controlled areas and classified workers. LSA scale is classed as a radioactive substance and its handling and disposal could present occupational health and hygiene risks. Operators must develop and put in place effective procedures that recognise the hazards, protect workers from harmful exposure, minimise interference with the environment and ensure that national and international regulations are followed.

- **Asbestos-containing materials (ACMs)** – these may be present in offshore installations built before 1999. The older an installation is, the more likely it is to contain higher-risk materials, e.g. lagging and boarding. Brake linings, gaskets, arc shields for electrical switchgear and external sheeting are further examples of ACMs that may be found offshore

The ageing offshore infrastructure requires increased maintenance and fabrication activities, so the potential for exposure to asbestos fibres is now greater. Exposure has occurred in several cases where asbestos has been poorly managed and subsequently disturbed, leading to disruptive and costly clean-up operations and enforcement action being taken.

REVISION QUESTIONS

7. Give the meaning of the terms Lower and Upper Flammability Limits.

8. Give the meaning of the classification 'carcinogenic'.

9. What are the main dangers associated with LPG?

10. What is the purpose of anti-foaming agents?

11. What term is applied to drilling wastes that contain naturally occurring radioactive materials (NORMs)?

(Suggested Answers are at the end.)

Risk Management Techniques Used in the Oil and Gas Industries

PURPOSES AND USES OF RISK ASSESSMENT TECHNIQUES

In their publication Risk assessment: A brief guide to controlling risks in the workplace (INDG163(rev 4)) the UK Health and Safety Executive (HSE) describe risk assessment as:

'not about creating huge amounts of paperwork, but rather about identifying sensible measures to control the risks in your workplace'.

Source: INDG163(rev4) Risk assessment: A brief guide to controlling risks in the workplace, HSE, 2014 (http://www.hse.gov.uk/pubns/indg163.pdf)

The five steps described in this system are:

STEP 1: Identify the hazards

▼

STEP 2: Identify the people who might be harmed and how

▼

STEP 3: Evaluate the risk and decide on precautions

▼

STEP 4: Record the significant findings

▼

STEP 5: Review and update as necessary

This method of risk assessment works well for less complex risks, and is suitable for most organisations where ranking of the risks is not a major requirement. But when the more complex risks associated with oil and gas production and processing have to be assessed, the technique used is likely to require far more depth and technical insight.

The UK **Offshore Installations (Safety Cases) Regulations 2005** require that:

- All hazards with the potential to cause a major accident have been identified.
- All major accident risks have been evaluated and measures have been, or will be, taken to control the major accident risks to ensure compliance with the relevant statutory provisions, i.e. a **compliance demonstration**.

The application of risk assessment should be proportionate to the magnitude of the risk. Because of the higher levels of risk in the oil and gas industries, we need to go further than the Five Steps approach and consider qualitative and quantified risk assessment techniques, the main objectives here being to identify **and rank** the risks and to examine risk reduction measures to determine which to use.

Qualitative and Quantified Risk Assessment

The risk assessment technique used should be able to rank the risks (risk ranking is not a significant detail of the Five Steps approach) so that the right reduction methods can be applied, and would probably progress in the following way:

- **Qualitative (Q)** – using qualitative methods to determine frequency and severity.
- **Semi-Quantitative (SQ)** – where frequency and severity are approximately quantified within ranges.
- **Quantified Risk Assessment (QRA)** – where full quantification is demonstrated.

As the assessment process moves through the stages, the level of detail will increase proportionate to the risk, taking into account the level of estimated risk within limits of tolerability, and the complexity of deciding on what (more) needs to be done to reduce the risk.

Determining the Right Method of Risk Assessment

Risk assessment is used to enable us to decide on appropriate risk controls, so assessors should be suitably senior, qualified and competent. Start with a qualitative model and enlarge the model (moving to SQ and QRA), as needed:

- Qualitative (Q):
  - If it **is** adequate for deciding on appropriate controls, use this method to assess and record the findings and recommendations.
  - If it is **not** adequate, **use SQ.**

- Semi-Quantitative (SQ):
  - If this (using more depth than Q) **is** adequate for deciding on appropriate controls, use SQ. Record the findings and recommendations.
  - If it is **not** adequate, first increase the depth of modelling of the risk assessment and see if it now meets requirements. If it does, record the findings and recommendations.
  - If it is not, **use QRA.**

- Quantified Risk Assessment (QRA):
  - If it **is** adequate, use QRA.
  - If it is **not**, increase the depth of the risk assessment model until it answers all questions. Record findings and recommendations.

MORE...

In its *Offshore Information Sheet No 3/2006,* the UK HSE gives more industry-specific guidance on how to determine which risk assessment method is appropriate.

You can access this document at: www.hse.gov.uk

THE STARTING-POINT APPROACH

Even using this method, it may still be necessary to upgrade the approach if it proves to be not detailed enough to determine suitable risk controls.

Examples of starting points could be:

- Large integrated platforms or nodal platforms in the North Sea are likely to have a combination of complexity and risk level requiring QRA.
- For less complex installations and those with smaller workforces, e.g. drilling installations, normally unattended installations (NIUs), etc. SQ could be suitable. In these cases, good-practice procedures will be largely relied upon to control such risks as transporting workers between installations (e.g. helicopter transfers).
- In cases where there are clear standards and benchmarks for design and risk reduction, Q will often be sufficient.
- For some stages of the lifecycle, where hazard identification can lead directly into specification of good-practice risk reduction measures, e.g. combined operations and decommissioning, Q or SQ may often be sufficient.

Risk Management Techniques Used in the Oil and Gas Industries

Hazard Identification

This is the underlying process of risk assessment and must be carried out thoroughly in all cases and models used. The main stages in the assessment are:

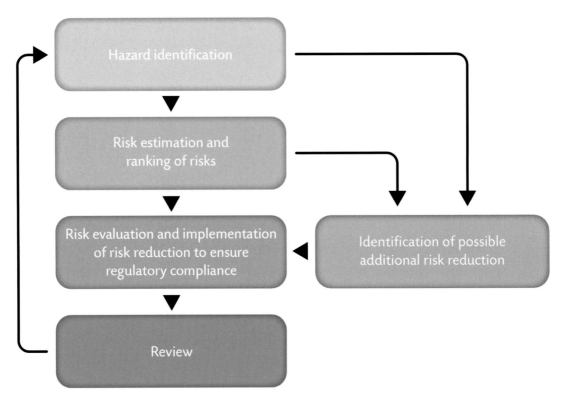

Source: Offshore Information Sheet No.3/2006, Guidance on Risk Assessment for Offshore Installations, HSE, 2006 (www.hse.gov.uk/offshore/sheet32006.pdf)

Risk Estimation and Ranking of Risks

Here, the likelihood (or frequency) of an adverse event, together with its consequences (severity) are estimated, the level of detail increasing as the model moves from Q, through SQ to QRA. A matrix is used (either 3 x 3 or – better – 5 x 5) to indicate risk levels – see following figure:

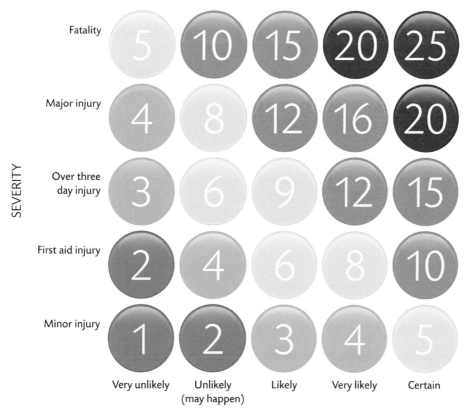

This now allows us to establish what more (if anything) needs to be done to reduce the risk. This can be determined, in simplest form, as:

1-4	LOW RISK	Maintain current levels of control.
5-10	MEDIUM RISK	Some further controls should be planned to reduce the risk further.
12-25	HIGH RISK	At this level work must STOP (or not begin if in planning stage) until further controls reduce the risk.

Do not forget the importance of the risk control measures already in place, as existing controls can be modified, rather than introducing new ones.

Also, different aspects of a single risk can be affected by different situations, and one example given by the UK HSE (*Offshore Information Sheet No 3/2006*) is the consideration of which stages of a scenario dominate its risk. In an emergency situation, for instance, would fatalities be immediate, be caused by escalation, or would they occur during escape, evacuation and rescue?

Risk Management Techniques Used in the Oil and Gas Industries

HOW RISK MANAGEMENT TOOLS ARE APPLIED

The following is an extract from the UK HSE publication *Managing for Health and Safety* with particular application to major hazard industries such as oil and gas processing.

"Industries where low-frequency, high-impact incidents would have catastrophic consequences must be properly managed, to ensure that the hazards are kept firmly in check. There should be illustrated and demonstrated risk reduction. Strong health and safety leadership, coupled with robust safety management systems, will ensure that best practice is shared and learning is disseminated from previous incidents. For major hazard sites, leadership on the key area of process safety is core. Board-level involvement and competence are essential; constant and active engagement in and promotion of process safety by the leadership sets a positive safety culture."

Source: Managing for Health and Safety, HSE, 2010 (www.hse.gov.uk/managing/regulators/regulators.pdf – note: this document is no longer available to non-regulators)

Risk management does what it says – manages risks (and doesn't just assess them).

All management systems, whether they are designed to manage health and safety or any other function, have the same common elements:

- **Plan** – implies having a considered policy.
- **Do** – concerns the arrangements for putting the plan into practice.
- **Check** – means it is necessary to assess or monitor performance.
- **Act** – means performance should be reviewed, leading to continuous improvement in the management system.

OHSAS 18001:2007 *Occupational Health and Management Systems: Specification* provides a recognisable management standard for certification. The following figure is based on that included in the standard.

OHSAS 18001:2007 Occupational Health and Management Systems: Specification – management system elements

The elements of the system described in **ILO-OSH-2001** *Guidelines on Occupational Health and Safety Management Systems* (**ILO, 2001**) are illustrated below. (The figure is reproduced by kind permission of the International Labour Organisation (ILO).) Note that the basic elements are very similar to OHSAS 18001 in concept. It is intended that the safety management system should be compatible with, or integrated into, other management systems within the organisation.

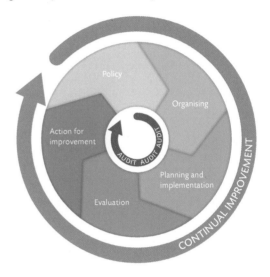

ILO-OSH-2001 Guidelines on Occupational Health and Safety Management Systems – management system elements

The real "management of risk" falls mainly within the Planning and Implementation stage. Adequate precautions must be provided to control the process risks and consideration should be given to three stages of the risk control system, as follows:

- Hazards and risks entering the organisation minimised at the **input stage**.
- Risks contained and controlled in the **process stage**.
- Risks prevented from going off-site, or in the products and services at the **output stage**.

Critical to the oil and gas process industries is the containment of hazardous materials and the effects of hazardous processes and systems, as well as effective maintenance (especially in harsh operating environments) and process-change procedures to ensure continuing plant integrity.

Applied in the project stage from concept, design and start-up, risk assessment and the development and implementation of risk controls will remain part of effective process safety management. Risk control systems will be needed for:

- **Physical resources**, such as:
  - Design, selection, purchase and construction of the oil or gas process workplace, i.e. the fields or rigs for exploration and production.
  - Design, selection, purchase and installation of oil and gas process plant; drilling and pumping equipment, etc.

- Design, selection and installation of safety-critical plant (deluge systems, etc.).
- Design and construction of workplace facilities, such as engineering and worker accommodation, welfare and recreation.
- Plant and substances used by others (e.g. contractors).

- **Human resources**, such as:
  - Recruitment and selection of oil and gas process and production workers.
  - Selection of suitable contractors and support staff.

- **Information**, including:
  - Health and safety standards to be followed in oil and gas.
  - Health and safety guidance for oil and gas.
  - Health and safety law and changes (revisions, etc).
  - Oil and gas process technical information relating to risk control.
  - Management information.
  - Development of a positive health and safety culture.

Of course, the risk control systems must be appropriate for, and proportionate to, the risks they are brought in to address. Where the risk assessment shows and introduces adequate risk controls at the **input stage**, attention must then move on to the **process stage** and controls needed to ensure continuing safe operation.

The hazards here are not necessarily hazards of design but hazards created by the workforce, their equipment, and how it is used, and hazards associated with oil and gas processing. Risk control systems will need to deal with the four main areas of risk:

- **Production workplace** – the field or rig and its associated facilities and support systems; safe access and egress; work environment; welfare facilities and accommodation; pipelines and structures, and electrical and communications installations.
- **Plant and substances** – the drilling and pumping and transportation systems of the oil and gas, how the oil and gas are stored and handled, and all materials in use at the process area.
- **Procedures** – organisational procedures such as work and shift patterns, job design and the way work is done (and managed).
- **People** – management and leadership, competence and placement of workers, training and health surveillance necessary.

It is important to focus not only on the risks inherent to the processes but also those "irregular" occurrences, such as breakdowns and emergencies. Events giving rise to foreseeable serious or imminent danger need particularly robust risk controls to be incorporated.

Concept of "As Low as Reasonably Practicable" (ALARP)

We have seen that it is a requirement to comply with all relevant health and safety law within oil and gas processing, and that both qualitative and quantitative risk assessment methods can be used. In all cases, there is a danger that the risk reduction methods may be decided on for the wrong reasons – based on affordability rather than compliance with the law; and always the danger to stop when the legal requirement has been seen to be met. This is where "as low as reasonably practicable" comes in.

ALARP covers risk at levels of some uncertainty:

- **Unacceptable risk** – risk cannot be justified at this level except in extraordinary circumstances (intolerable).
- **ALARP** (tolerability region) – at the higher-risk end, risk may be undertaken only if a benefit is desired, and where risk reduction is impracticable, i.e. grossly disproportionate to the benefits gained. At the lower-risk end, risk is tolerable if the cost to reduce it would outweigh the benefits.
- **Acceptable risk** – where it is necessary to demonstrate risk remains this low, there is no need for detailed working to demonstrate ALARP. At the lower end, this is negligible risk (tolerable).

All risks should be reduced to ALARP, and in some cases cost-benefit analysis may be needed to determine the appropriate level of controls. All levels of risk should be compared to oil and gas industry guidance and best practice.

Risk Management Techniques Used in the Oil and Gas Industries

Other Risk Management Tools

Different approaches may be taken depending on the nature of the operations (offshore exploration or onshore refining and storage) and the sectors or areas they actually operate in. Methods include HAZOP, HAZID, FMEA, etc.; qualitative and quantitative risk analysis; security or terrorist management, or more specific and local hazard and risk analysis in pipelines; dispersion modelling for fire, blast and explosions; and blast resistance design and construction. Evacuation planning is also important, as is the correct siting of facilities used to assess the location of buildings/modules based on known hazards.

We will look briefly at some of these techniques.

- **HAZOP (Hazard and Operability Studies)** – first used by ICI in the 1960s to identify hazards in the design of their chemical plants. This technique identifies potential hazards so that suitable precautions can be introduced to control them, and is particularly useful in the design of chemical or other hazardous installations and processes. It is carried out by a multi-disciplinary team with expertise in design of the installation, commissioning, production and process operations, maintenance of the facilities and ongoing requirements for health and safety.

  HAZOP applies guide words (e.g. no, more, less) to process variables such as temperature, flow and pressure.

  Where HAZOP identifies a significant risk, it will go on to specify what actions should be taken to reduce the risk to an acceptable level. This may involve changing the design, altering installation criteria, different maintenance and inspection requirements, or the introduction of particular safe operating procedures. The following table gives an idea of how the guidewords are used.

Guideword	Possible deviations
No or *None* or *Not*	No flow of oil. No flow of gas. No electric current. No supply pressure.
More (quantitative increase) or *Less* (quantitative decrease)	Relate to any quantitative increase or decrease in such parameters, e.g. more flow, pressure, electric current, viscosity, volume, weight, temperature, dimension, etc.
Part of (qualitative decrease) or *As well as* (quantitative increase)	For example, one or more compounds or mixtures missing.
Reverse (opposite of intention)	Reverse flow (i.e. backflow).
Other criteria	• What other things can occur? • Instrumentation fault/failure. • Corrosion of components. • Failure of pressure vessel or pipework. • Sampling and monitoring activities. • Venting and system-relief activation. • Service failure (cooling, lubrication, air). • Maintenance activities. • Hydrocarbon releases. • Flammable atmospheres. • Static electricity.

- HAZID (Hazard Identification) – uses "brainstorming" techniques driven by the use of key words appropriate to the study being undertaken. HAZID is useful when considering changes to existing plant layout, the assessor often mapping hazards and their locations on a walk-through of the facility. Where this practical method cannot be used, then computer programmes can be used instead. As the name suggests, it is a hazard identification exercise that is intended to pick out as many hazards as possible for later risk assessment.

- FMEA (Failure Modes and Effects Analysis) – a technique often used to calculate the possibility of failure or malfunction, usually of components in an assembly or piece of equipment, and to calculate the possibility of failure or malfunction of the assembly or equipment itself. This is an example of an inductive analysis, sometimes referred to as a "bottom-up" approach.

It lists individual components and items and looks both at their individual failure and their individual failure effects on the whole system. It questions performance by asking: "If this item fails, what will the result be?" Again, used in the design stages of a new process it attempts to find potential problems before they actually happen.

It asks the basic questions:

- In what way can each component fail?
- What might cause this type of failure?
- What could be the effects of this type of failure?
- How serious could the failure be?
- How is each failure detected?

It uses technical drawings of the assembly and its components, and describes clearly the complete function of all the components and their bearing on the overall function of the assembly.

INDUSTRY-RELATED PROCESS SAFETY STANDARDS

Inherently safe and risk-based design concepts, and engineering codes and good practice are the foundations for onshore and offshore operational safety.

Inherently safer design concepts are particularly useful for risk reduction and are highly recognised and recommended by safety professionals as a first choice in process-design practices.

GLOSSARY

INHERENTLY SAFER DESIGNS
Designs where the design engineers use a variety of techniques to achieve risk reduction through design ("design it out" principle).

Such methods include:

- Hazard elimination – as it suggests, get rid of the hazards as a first priority, instead of accepting and reducing them with risk reduction strategies after assessment.

- Consequence reduction – if the hazards can't be eliminated, find less hazardous solutions to accomplish the same design objective using techniques such as reducing exposure to a hazard, or reducing the number of hazardous materials kept in stock. We could also substitute hazardous with less hazardous materials.

- Likelihood reduction – here we attempt to reduce the likelihood (the probability) of a hazardous event from happening by techniques using simplification and clarity (lowering the likelihood of an initiating event) and layers of redundancy of safeguards (to reduce event progression).

While prevention, detection and mitigation are all considered for inherent safety, the emphasis should be on prevention. For example, moving the proposed location of a flammable liquid storage tank away from accommodation areas or, onshore, away from a public boundary around an installation, may greatly reduce the consequences of a release and could also reduce or even eliminate the costs of providing added protection systems that may be needed if not safely sited elsewhere.

Inherent safety includes the consideration of more than just design features of a process. The principles include human safety factors, in particular the opportunities for human error given the design and operating conditions and parameters.

Risk Management Techniques Used in the Oil and Gas Industries

Examples of inherent safety in action:

Error-Likely Situation	Proposed Solution
Controls too difficult to access.	Work to reduce clutter to give more working space.
Displays too complicated to understand easily; difficult to interpret information displayed.	Improve design and layout to reduce the chance of human error.

Summary of Inherently Safer Design Concepts

HAZARD ELIMINATION

Concept – eliminate hazards as first priority, rather than accept and deal with risks.

Methods:

- Eliminate use of a hazardous material.
- Substitute with a less hazardous material.
- Discontinue the operation.

CONSEQUENCE REDUCTION

Concept – where elimination is not practicable, find less hazardous solutions to accomplish the same design objectives by focusing on the consequences of an adverse event.

Methods:

- Reduce quantities of hazardous materials.
- Provide a curbed area with a drain to contain and evacuate a spill, and produce a smaller pool area of a spill.
- Separate the operation (from critical areas) by adequate spacing to reduce exposure to adjacent operations and personnel.

LIKELIHOOD REDUCTION

Concept – where hazards can't be completely eliminated and after consideration of consequence reduction, consider ways to reduce the likelihood of events occurring.

Methods:

- Reduce the potential for human error through simplicity of design.
- Control ignition sources.
- Provide redundancy and alarms.

Sources of Written, Recognised Good Practice

- (UK) HSE Guidance and Approved Codes of Practice (ACoPS).
- National or local government guidance.
- Standards from international or national accredited providers (BS, CEN, CENELEC, ISO, IEC, etc).
- Industry-specific or sector guidance from trade federations, professional institutions.

Other sources of good practice, often unwritten, may be acceptable to national or local competent authorities providing they satisfy necessary conditions, such as the well-defined and established standard practices adopted in a specific industry or sector.

Good practice may change over time as technology improves the degree of control over a process or operation (which may provide an opportunity to use elimination and advanced engineering controls), cost changes (perhaps allowing control at lower costs), or because changes occur in management practices.

Good practice may also change because of increased knowledge about the hazard and/or a change in the acceptability of the level of risk control achieved by the existing good practice.

In the definition of good practice, "law" refers to that law acceptable to the situation in question (determined by national or local competent authorities); such law may set absolute standards (e.g. 'shall'), or its requirements may be qualified in some other, less stringent way (e.g. 'practicable' or 'reasonably practicable').

'Good practice', as understood and used by the UK HSE, can be distinguished from the term 'best practice', which usually means a standard of risk control above the legal minimum.

CONCEPT OF HAZARD REALISATION

This concept is not only about asking "*What if?*" but also taking a more detailed look to attempt to know the "*What if?*" before it actually happens. We can use as an example the loss of containment of hydrocarbons that would lead to ignition; which leads to fire or explosion; which leads to damage and injury to workers.

Key Risk Assessment Issues Relating to Loss of Containment Causing Hydrocarbon Releases (HCRs)

- Major source of HCRs: system piping (piping, flanges, valves) and instrumentation (i.e. Small Bore Tubing systems (SBT)).
- Main operating systems experiencing HCRs: gas compression.
- Biggest operational cause: wrongly-fitted equipment.
- Next biggest operational cause: incorrect or improper operation (human factors).
- Main procedural cause: failure to comply with procedures (human factors).

The UK HSE figures reveal that in an eight-year period from 2000/2001, instruments (SBT) were the largest single contributor to HCRs greater than 25kg. Furthermore, they show that inspections and surveys on SBT systems suggest that 26% of fittings examined contained faults, e.g. under-tightness, incorrect or mismatched components, leaks, incorrect or poor installation, etc. and that this failure has been consistent since 2001.

(Source: Offshore Information Sheet No.2/2009, Hydrocarbon Releases (HCRs) Offshore, HSE, 2009 (www.hse.gov.uk/offshore/infosheets/is2-2009.pdf))

What we have detailed above are the causes of hydrocarbon releases, which must be addressed by risk controls. Our "*What if?*" scenario needs to show, based on the size and location of the hydrocarbon release, what the potential results, in damage and injury/loss of life, could be. This potential will enable us to determine priorities around which we introduce the risk controls to prevent the hydrocarbon releases.

We start with the **worst-case scenario**:

What?
- A major HCR (e.g. above 25kg).

Where?
- From piping or instrumentation.
- On a gas compression unit.
- In close proximity to a welfare or accommodation facility.
- With uncontrolled ignition sources in the vicinity (e.g. electrical fault).

When?
- At a time when occupation of that facility is greatest (e.g. in a canteen at a main mealtime), e.g. 34 workers (50% of staff).
- The deluge system is on manual override owing to maintenance work.

How?
- Poorly maintained piping, or instrumentation with incorrect fittings and not correctly tightened.

Why?
- No planned preventive maintenance or inspection programme.
- No detection equipment for hydrocarbon releases.
- No emergency action plan in place for hydrocarbon releases.
- No fire-fighting equipment in the vicinity of the release (or fire-fighting equipment empty/not maintained/moved).
- Poor fire-fighting training for personnel.
- Poor response by personnel/lack of response training.
- Lack of management leadership decisions.

Hopefully, this is an exaggerated circumstance, and many of the variables will already have been dealt with by the design of the installation (i.e. no welfare or accommodation near gas compressors) but the analysis can offer the opportunity to examine the realisation of this type of hydrocarbon release hazard. How likely is it (what is the probability) that all of these events (and we could possibly discover more by a greater in-depth analysis) will actually happen at the same time? Were they to happen, what would be the severity (the consequences) of the release?

Again, we start with the **worst-case scenario**:

What?
- Hydrocarbon release is ignited by electrical fault.
- Explosion and fire engulf the canteen.
- All 34 workers in the canteen are lost.
- Gas compression unit destroyed by blast.
- Gas process operation lost – long downtime.

Why?
- No warning of hydrocarbon release.
- No water from the deluge system.
- Long release duration.
- Fire-fighting media not available.
- All on-shift workers in other areas.
- No trained response team.
- No emergency action plan or EER (Escape, Evacuation and Rescue).
- Time taken to get response teams to location too long, etc.

You need to continue this process to discover all the consequences, however minor.

As you work down the possibilities within each scenario, you begin to eliminate or reduce some of the consequences **and** the probability of them occurring. For instance, if there are **no** welfare or accommodation facilities in proximity to the gas compressors, then this leg of the trail will not be there, and we will not lose 50% of our crew. If the fire deluge system is **not** on manual override, water **will** be available to deal with a fire, etc.

Risk Management Techniques Used in the Oil and Gas Industries

CONCEPT OF RISK CONTROL
BARRIER MODELS

As well as the risk controls we have looked at, we could also consider placing barriers between the event and its results, or placing a barrier between the hazard and its realisation.

An example given by the UK HSE in the *Offshore Information Sheet No 3/2006* illustrates the concept of using barriers in a **bow-tie diagram**, which represents all of the initiators of the scenario and the consequences. Between the initiators and the consequences, barriers are placed that should prevent, control, or mitigate the outcome of the event. In this case, such barriers are known as Lines of Defence (LOD) or Layers of Protection (LOP).

Reference numbers can be assigned to barriers which are common to several event initiators for a particular scenario (see barrier 1a in the following diagram, which comes between two initiators and the release) as well as those common to several scenarios.

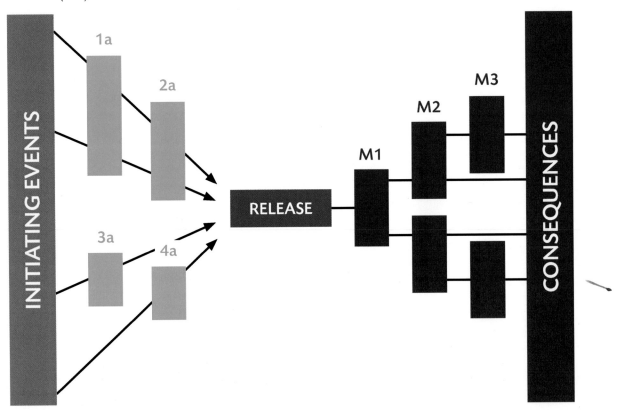

Example Barriers:	Example Barriers:
• Plant layout	• Detection system
• Construction standards	• ESD (Emergency Shut Down)
• Inspection	• Active protection
• Instrumentation	• Passive protection
	• EER (Escape, Evacuation & Rescue)

Based on Offshore Information Sheet No.3/2006, Guidance on Risk Assessment for Offshore Installations, HSE, 2006 (www.hse.gov.uk/offshore/sheet32006.pdf)

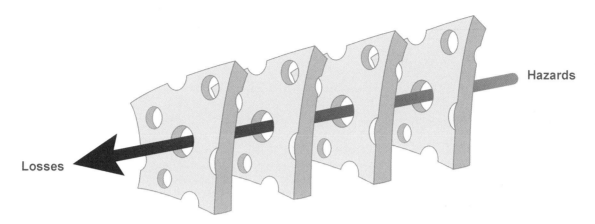

Swiss Cheese Barrier Model

USE OF MODELLING

Thermal Radiation Output, Blast Zones for Risk Assessment

A major objective behind optimised plant layout is the avoidance of incidents leading to fire or explosion and the protection of people, assets and reputation. This requires good separation between hazardous and vulnerable areas. Separation can be determined by the use of modelling systems, which will also show the value of minimisation of equipment, liquid hydrocarbon inventory in process equipment, vulnerability through selection of the type of equipment and exposure of people through process-related complexity and maintenance.

As well as the bow-tie system, models use barriers such as the Swiss-cheese model, shown above. In this system, barriers are used between hazards and consequences (hazard losses or hazard realisation). Such barriers could be design features, shutdown and alarm systems, operations and procedures, etc.

Modelling

There now exists a body of data and sophisticated modelling software that can, for example, estimate:

- Evaporation rate of flammable liquids (e.g. from a spill).
- Dispersion of leaking vapours/gases, including the likely concentrations at given points on and off-site, taking account of vapour density and any propensity to settle in low-lying areas.
- Likely types, effects and scale of any fires and explosions – the rate of pressure rise, maximum pressure, intensity of thermal radiation (for different fire types) and other parameters can be estimated.

Modelling is a valuable predictive tool used to explore the significance of possible major hazard scenarios and so help decision-making. Apart from the information already identified above, it also enables:

- Identification of the key contributors to explosion risks – this helps prioritisation.
- Exploration of the effectiveness of existing preventive and protective measures – which could help justify the adequacy of your existing controls.

Modelling is also obviously useful in safety case justifications.

There are many modelling systems available and some are substance-specific, e.g. LNG.

REVISION QUESTIONS

12. Which four elements are common to health and safety, as well as general, management systems?

13. What are the four main areas of risk to be dealt with in oil and gas processing risk control systems?

14. In risk control barrier models (e.g. bow-tie) between what criteria are barriers placed, and what are the barriers called?

(Suggested Answers are at the end.)

An Organisation's Documented Evidence

> **KEY INFORMATION**
>
> - Organisations must have documented evidence that their safety systems are adequate, including safety cases and safety reports, which can be used to meet both legal requirements and best practice.

EXAMPLES OF DOCUMENTED EVIDENCE

Organisations may be required to produce evidence that an installation is adequately safe.

These are often called either safety cases (offshore) or safety reports (onshore).

WHERE SUCH DOCUMENTED EVIDENCE IS USED

Safety Cases

Safety cases are legally required in some countries, and in the UK the **Offshore Installations (Safety Case) Regulations 2005 (OSCR)** require operators of all installations to prepare a safety case where their operations will be located in British waters and in UK-designated areas of the continental shelf. It will be an offence to operate in these areas without a safety case that has been submitted to the UK Health and Safety Executive. Different requirements will apply to installations used for producing oil and gas and those used for other purposes, such as drilling, exploration or for providing accommodation.

A single duty-holder has the duty to submit the safety case for each type of installation, usually the **operator** of a production installation and the **owner** of a non-production installation.

NOTIFICATION

Operators of all new offshore production installations must notify the HSE (or, in other countries, their competent authority) at the early design stage (see above). Notification is also necessary if a production installation is to be moved to a new location, or if a non-production installation (such as a drilling rig) is to be converted for production purposes.

Further notification is required if installations engage in combined operations, to cover all aspects of those combined operations. Particular attention here is on co-operation and co-ordination between the installations.

A **safety case** must follow the notification, and production cannot begin until the HSE or other national competent authority accepts the safety case. Where an installation that is to be moved already has a safety case, a revision of it must be submitted for acceptance. A revised safety case must also be submitted and accepted before a fixed installation can be dismantled. If a non-production installation is to be moved into UK waters to be operated there, its owner must submit a safety case and have it accepted before it can be moved there.

ACCEPTANCE

The HSE or national competent authority will "accept" a safety case (or a revision of one) when duty-holders demonstrate and describe specified matters to the HSE's satisfaction, i.e. in their judgment, all measures described in the safety case are **likely** to achieve compliance – they do not have to be satisfied that it **will** be achieved. This will be confirmed in post-acceptance programmes of inspection and enforcement. It must always be understood that acceptance of a safety case does not guarantee the safety of the installation, or its operators.

Safety Reports

Safety reports may be required in various countries, and are needed in the UK to ensure safety of sites under the **Control of Major Accident Hazards Regulations 1999**. Writing the safety report demonstrates how you meet the duties set out for operators in these Regulations.

Safety reports must demonstrate that safety measures are in place to prevent the occurrence of major accidents associated with (specified) amounts of hazardous substances on the site, and to limit their consequences should they occur. There is also emphasis on measures in place to protect the environment.

The safety report should be submitted to the local office of the HSE, or national competent authority, who, together with other national agencies, such as environmental enforcing agencies, will work together to assess the report.

PURPOSE OF DOCUMENTED EVIDENCE

Safety cases are required to ensure that those involved in offshore activities design, construct, commission and operate their facilities in order to reduce the risks to the health and safety of those working on the offshore installations or in connected activities to as low as reasonably practicable (ALARP).

The safety case is a document that demonstrates (to the duty holder and the national competent authority) that the duty holder is capable of controlling major accident risks effectively. It is a core document for checking by both parties that risk controls and safety management systems are in place and operate as they should.

Like the safety case, a **safety report** contributes to preventing major accidents on sites having specified amounts of hazardous substances, normally onshore.

It demonstrates that you have measures in place to prevent major accidents and limit consequences to people and the environment. It examines the site activities systematically, as well as the potential for major accidents and what is, or is not going to be done to prevent them. Importantly, it shows that you have used a systematic process to arrive at the risk controls, showing the depth to which you have gone to develop them. It shows you can correct any shortcomings.

TYPICAL CONTENT OF SAFETY CASES AND SAFETY REPORTS

Typical content includes:

- Identification of **major accident hazards** using risk assessments (Q, SQ, QRA), bow-tie diagrams, etc. and criteria from previous operations and incident records, as well as design drawings and calculations. The impacts of potential major accident hazards should be analysed and summarised, and should identify:
    - Each hazard scenario.
    - Threats to safety and what causes them.
    - Barriers to prevent those threats.
    - Consequences of each threat, were it realised.
    - Recovery measures required.
    - Factors that could escalate the hazard, or its consequences.
- Evaluation of **major accident risks** and measures taken (or to be taken) to control those risks, using details of all existing "designed-in" precautionary and safety measures. Existing and previous risk controls should be included, then evaluated to see if these are adequate, or if further risk controls are required to demonstrate ALARP. This would include:
    - Identify each hazard/incident scenario.
    - Assess frequency criteria.
    - Assess consequence criteria.
    - Assess occupied and unoccupied locations as separate criteria.
    - Assess Evacuation, Escape and Rescue (EER) facilities and requirements.
    - For higher risks, assess individually.
    - Identify and assess the risk control measures proposed to achieve ALARP.
- Arrangements for **audit and audit reports** with a plan showing the type of audit (internal, external), how often they will be carried out, in what areas they will be conducted, how recommendations will be dealt with and actioned, and who will be responsible for completion.
- Having an adequate **safety management system** in place, including the management of contractors and sub-contractors. Selection criteria and approved lists of contractors would be held, together with all returned data from contractors (such as safety questionnaires confirming competence, insurances, etc.).

- **Major-accident prevention policies** – in the case of safety reports these would need supporting information from the safety management system.
- Identification of the **safety-critical elements** that are in place to manage major accident hazards (scenarios, possible causes, controls, recovery systems).
- Details of the **emergency plan**. This would include layout drawings of the installation, showing locations of all safety and emergency equipment, control points (e.g. control room, radio room, etc.), isolation and shut-off controls, safe access routes and escape ladders, access to boats and manning and launch procedures.

The actual detailed content depends on the installation.

Safety Cases

In some countries, all production operators must have a safety case in place, which clearly identifies all installations covered by it and, in the specific case of a **production installation**, which shows:

- Details of the operator (name and address).
- A design notification that includes:
    - A description of the design process from initial concept to the submitted design (and the design philosophy used to guide the process).
    - A description of the design concept with diagrams and summary of other design options considered.
    - How the design concept will ensure legal compliance.
    - How the design concept will ensure that risks with the potential to cause a major accident are reduced (to ALARP).
    - The criteria used to select the chosen design concept and how the selection was made.
- The design notification is to include a description of:
    - The principal systems on the installation.
    - The installation layout.
    - The process technology to be used.
    - The principal features of any pipeline.
    - Any petroleum-bearing reservoir intended to be exploited using the installation.
    - The basis of design for any wells to be connected to the installation.
- A summary of how any safety representatives for that installation were consulted with regard to the revision, review or preparation of the safety case, how their views were taken into account, etc.

An Organisation's Documented Evidence

The safety case details continue with:

- A description, with suitable diagrams, of the main and secondary structure of the installation and its materials.
- A description of its plant (machinery, equipment or appliance such as drilling, well maintenance and production testing plant).
- A suitable plan of the location of the installation and of anything connected to it.
- Particulars of the meteorological and oceanographic conditions to which the installation may foreseeably be subjected.
- The properties of the sea bed and subsoil at its location.
- Particulars of the particular types of operation and activities in connection with the operation that the installation is capable of performing.
- The maximum number of persons expected to be on the installation at one time and for whom accommodation is to be provided.
- Particulars of the plant and arrangements for the control of well operations, including those to:
  - Control pressure in a well.
  - Prevent the uncontrolled release of hazardous substances.
  - Minimise the effects of damage to sub-sea equipment by drilling equipment.
- A description of any pipeline with the potential to cause a major accident, including:
  - The fluid it conveys.
  - Its dimensions and layout.
  - Its contained volume at declared maximum allowable operating pressure.
  - Any apparatus and works intended to secure safety.
- A description of how the duty-holder has ensured (or will ensure) that people on the installation are protected from fires and explosion and for ensuring effective emergency response.
- A description of the arrangements made for protecting persons on the installation from toxic gas at all times other than during any period while they may need to remain on the installation following an incident that is beyond immediate control.

- A description of the measures or arrangements for the protection of persons on the installation from explosion, fire, heat, smoke, toxic gas or fumes during any period they may need to remain on the installation following an incident that is beyond immediate control, and for enabling such persons to be evacuated from the installation where necessary, including:
  - Temporary refuge.
  - Routes from locations where persons may be present to temporary refuge and for egress therefrom to points from where the installation may be evacuated.
  - Means of evacuation at those points.
  - Facilities within the temporary refuge for the monitoring and control of the incident and for organising evacuation.
- A description of the main requirements in the specification of the design of the installation and its plant, which shall include:
  - Any limits for safe operation or use specified therein.
  - A description of how the duty-holder has or will comply with **any specific requirements of the national competent authority**.
  - A description of how the duty-holder, in relation to a pipeline has or will ensure their operation within safe limits, or
  - Where he is not also the operator in relation to a pipeline, has or will co-operate with the operator to ensure their operation within safe limits.
- Particulars of any combined operations that may involve the installation, including:
  - A summary of the arrangements in place for co-ordinating the management systems of all duty-holders involved in such a combined operation.
  - A summary of the arrangements in place for joint review of the safety aspects of any such combined operation by all duty-holders involved, which shall include the identification of hazards with the potential to cause a major accident and the assessment of risks that may arise during any such combined operation.
  - The plant likely to be used during such combined operations.
  - The likely impact any such combined operation may have on the installations involved.

Safety Reports

Safety reports make "demonstrations" and the information they contain should relate to:

- The management system and the organisation of the establishment with a view to major accident prevention.
- Description of the environment of the establishment.
- Description of the installation.
- Hazard identification, consequence assessment, risk analysis and prevention methods.
- Measures of prevention and intervention to limit the consequences of a major accident.

REVISION QUESTION

15. What main areas does a safety case/safety report cover?

(Suggested Answers are at the end.)

SUMMARY

This element has dealt with health, safety and environmental management issues facing those in control of oil and gas process operations. In particular, it has:

- Explained the purpose of investigating accidents and the procedures available, including a discussion of the lessons that can be learned from previous incidents and which can be used to improve health and safety in the oil and gas industries.

- Explained the hazards that are inherent in oil and gas processing from the extraction, storage and processing of raw materials and products, and given definitions of specific terminology used. The properties and hazards of gases and other substances, as well as materials and additives used in or created by the processing of oil and gas, were discussed.

- Outlined the risk management and risk assessment techniques available.

- Explained the purpose and content of an organisation's documented evidence to provide a convincing and valid argument that a system is adequately safe in the oil and gas industries. This included details of the use of safety cases and safety reports.

Exam Skills

INTRODUCTION

To pass the NEBOSH International Technical Certificate in Oil and Gas Operational Safety you need to perform well during the exam. You have two hours, and your performance will be related to two key factors:

- The amount that you can remember about the elements you've studied; and
- Your success in applying that knowledge in an exam situation.

Being good at both aspects is essential. Being calm under exam pressure is pointless if you do not have a good knowledge of the information required to answer the exam questions.

Here, we will consider some practical guidelines that can be used to increase success in the exam. Then you will find Exam Skills questions to answer at the end of each element, starting with this one.

EXAM REQUIREMENTS

The exam consists of two sections:

- Section 1 contains one question which is likely to consist of a number of sub parts. This question in total is worth 20 marks.
- Section 2 contains ten questions, with each question being worth eight marks.

There is no choice of questions in the exam – all questions are compulsory. The exam in total lasts two hours and NEBOSH recommend that you spend about:

- Half an hour on Section 1; and
- One-and-a-half hours on Section 2.

EXAM TECHNIQUE

In the exam, candidates can often struggle because they have not understood the question that is being asked. They can interpret questions wrongly and, as such, provide an answer for the question they think is being asked but, in reality, is not. To try to avoid this, let's look at a step-by-step approach that you can adopt when answering exam questions:

1. The first step is to read the question carefully. Be sure you know exactly what type of information the question wants you to give in your answer. Highlight or underline on the exam paper the key words in the question, such as the command words (identify, outline, etc.) and the question topic.

2. Monitor the time. The 20-mark question in the first section should take around 25 minutes to answer, with five minutes' reviewing time. The eight-mark questions in Section 2 should take around eight minutes to answer. This will leave an accumulated time of ten minutes at the end of Section 2 to review your answers.

3. Next, consider the marks available. For each mark to be awarded the examiner will expect a piece of information to award the mark against.

4. The next stage is to develop a plan – there are various ways to do this. Remind yourself again of the content of the question. Focus on key words that you have underlined on the examination paper to make sure you answer the question set. The answer plan is your aide-mémoire and can take the form of a list, or a mind map that helps you unload information quickly and makes sure you have enough factors (or points) in your answer that will attract the available marks. Keep re-reading the question to ensure your answer plan is going to answer the question asked.

Exam Skills

5. When composing your answer it is essential that you pay proper attention to the command word (e.g. outline, describe, identify, explain) that has been used in the question. Candidates lose marks if they take the wrong approach. Remember, you made a list to help your memory. NEBOSH will not be asking for a list anywhere on the paper, so if you reproduce your answer plan in the answer, you will not gain the maximum available marks. The command word informs you about the amount and depth of information the examiner is expecting you to provide on the factors you have listed in your answer plan.

COMMAND WORDS AND THEIR MEANINGS

Below are a few of the most commonly used command words with their meaning:

- **Identify** – select and name.
- **Outline** – give the key features of. You need to give a brief description of something, or a brief explanation of reasons why. This is less depth than 'Explain' or 'Describe' – a great amount of depth and detail is not required.
- **Describe** – provide an in-depth description, a word picture of what the thing is, what it looks like, how it works, etc. – a detailed account.
- **Explain** – provide a detailed explanation – reasons why, reasons for, how it works, etc; again, detail is required. 'Explain' is usually used in a subdivided question, so the detail required is tested in a narrowed-down field.

When it comes to the exam, make sure you indicate clearly your Answer Plan and your Final Answer for the examiner.

EXAM SKILLS PRACTICE

At the end of each element there is an Exam Skills question (or two) for you to attempt, with guidance on how to approach the question, a suggested Answer Plan, and a Possible Answer. All of the points listed in the Answer Plan would attract marks and you will see most of them developed in the possible answer itself.

Remember that when answering exam questions, information from additional reading and personal experience may be included. Examining bodies encourage this and it will enhance your answers.

There is a time estimate at the beginning of each Exam Skills activity. Don't worry if the activity takes you a little longer than this – the timings are just there as a rough guide.

QUESTION

a) Explain the meaning of the term "flash point". (2)

b) Identify the three classifications within flammability. (3)

c) Explain where the flammable range exists in a fuel/air mixture. (3)

30

APPROACHING THE QUESTION

- Using the system we have covered, the first thing to do is read the question carefully. You are asked this question in three parts – to provide an explanation of what 'flash point' means; identify the three classifications of flammability; and explain how flammability falls within flammable ranges. You should structure your approach in your Answer Plan.

- Next consider the marks available. In this question there are eight marks; we can see that the question is split into three different parts, with marks shown for each part. The question should take you around eight minutes to answer.

- Now highlight the key words. In this case, this might look like this:

   a) Explain the meaning of the term "flash point". (2)

   b) Identify the three classifications within flammability. (3)

   c) Explain where the flammable range exists in a fuel/air mixture. (3)

- Read the question again – make sure you understand it.

- Following this, the next stage is to develop a plan. Remember, a plan can be completed in various ways, but it could consist of the following:

SUGGESTED ANSWER

Plan

Flash point	Lowest temp. – vapour given off – can be ignited
Classification of flammability	Flammable Highly flammable Extremely flammable
Flammable range	LFL – Minimum concentration – 'too lean' UFL – Maximum concentration – 'too rich' Flammable range lies between

Now have a go at the question yourself.

Exam Skills

POSSIBLE ANSWER BY EXAM CANDIDATE

(a) "Flash point" is the lowest temperature at which sufficient vapour is given off to "flash" – that is, ignite momentarily (and not carry on burning) when a source of ignition is applied to the vapour.

(b) Flammability falls into three distinct classifications:
- Extremely flammable – flash point below 0° Celsius.
- Highly flammable – flash point between 0° and 21°.
- Flammable – flash point between 21° and 55° (inclusive).

(c) The lower flammable limit is the minimum concentration of fuel in air that will allow combustion to occur (below this, the mixture is too lean).

The upper flammable limit is the maximum concentration of fuel in air that will allow combustion to occur (above this, the mixture is too rich).

The flammable range lies between these limits.

REASONS FOR POOR MARKS ACHIEVED BY CANDIDATES IN EXAM

- Not answering the question at all. If you do not attempt all questions required you cannot get any marks.
- Not following a structured approach: remember, the question has three distinct parts, and asked for explain, identify and explain, so a list would not gain maximum marks.
- Giving lots of other information not relevant to the question.

HYDROCARBON PROCESS SAFETY 1

ELEMENT
2

LEARNING OUTCOMES

On completion of this element, you should be able to demonstrate understanding of the content by applying what you have learnt to familiar and unfamiliar situations. In particular, you should be able to:

1 Explain the principles of assessing and managing contractors, including the roles of parties involved.

2 Outline the tools, standards, measurement, competency requirements and controls applicable to Process Safety Management (PSM) in the oil and gas industries.

3 Explain the role and purpose of a permit-to-work system.

4 Explain the key principles of safe shift handover.

5 Explain the importance of safe plant operation and maintenance of hydrocarbon-containing equipment and processes.

6 Outline the hazards, risks and controls to ensure safe start-up and shut-down of hydrocarbon-containing equipment and processes.

Contents

Contractor Management

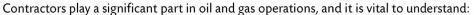

KEY INFORMATION

Contractors play a significant part in oil and gas operations, and it is vital to understand:

- The scale of contractor use.
- Contractor management, ownership and site supervision/representation.
- Safe handover and the hazards associated with it.

SCALE OF CONTRACTOR USE

A contractor is anyone you bring into the organisation to carry out work on your behalf who is not an employee/worker directly employed by the company. Contractors are widely used to carry out construction, installation, repairs, maintenance, demolition and deconstruction. Often, support vessels and diving services, as well as work on drilling and exploration rigs, are run by contracted service companies. Accidents involving contractors are common in these areas.

It is quite usual to have more than one contractor on an installation at one time, so it is important to understand and control how the work they do affects directly employed workers and other persons on the installation.

CONTRACTOR MANAGEMENT, OWNERSHIP AND REPRESENTATION

The work that contractors do must be covered by your own usual methods of safe working, or accidents will happen. To achieve this:

- Ensure the hazards of the contractors' job have been identified and steps taken to reduce the risks.
- Ensure a representative of the owner or operator is available to make sure contractors follow the rules of the installation.
- Ensure all contractor workers know who the site or installation contact person is, and how they can be contacted.
- Have procedures in place that ensure close and safe working with contractors at all times.

Poor communication is one of the major causes of accidents for contractors working on a site or installation, especially if directly employed workers are not aware of who the contractors are and what they are doing there. Likewise, the contractors must know the dangers of the site or installation.

For these reasons, contractors must be included in all health and safety procedures of the operation, and are required to adhere to employers' working practices and procedures, permit-to-work systems, etc. Good practice may be assured from your own directly employed workers, but don't necessarily expect it from contractors. For this reason, induction training for the site or installation is critical.

Induction training is carried out at each onshore and offshore installation, and each company has its own induction process. Induction training must therefore be carried out for contractors at each installation, as induction programmes will vary. To support this, contractor meetings should be held both onshore and offshore before contractors begin any work at any location.

Contractors should be made aware that failure to comply with induction training, employers' safe systems of work, permit procedures, etc. can result in disciplinary action being taken against individuals, as well as contract penalties being imposed on the main contract management.

Contractor Management

The UK Health and Safety Executive demonstrates a simple five-step approach to managing contractors:

Managing Contractors - Five Steps

STEP 1 – PLANNING

- Define the job
- Identify the hazards
- Assess the risks
- Eliminate or reduce the risks
- Specify health and safety conditions
- Discuss with contractor (if selected)

STEP 2 – CHOOSING A CONTRACTOR

- What safety and technical competence is needed?
- Ask questions (use questionnaire)
- Get evidence
- Go through information about:
    - the job
    - the site or installation and site rules
- Ask for a safety method statement
- Decide whether sub-contracting is acceptable. If it is, how will health and safety be ensured?

STEP 3 – CONTRACTORS WORKING ON SITE

- All contractors sign in and out
- Name a site or installation contact
- Reinforce health and safety information and site rules
- Check the job and allow work to begin

STEP 4 – KEEPING A CHECK

- Assess the degree of contact needed:
    - how is the job going?
    - as planned?
    - is the contractor working safely as agreed?
    - have any incidents occurred?
    - have there been changes in personnel?
- Are any special arrangements required?

STEP 5 – REVIEWING THE WORK

- Review the job and the contractor:
    - how effective was your planning?
    - how did the contractor perform?
    - how did the job go?
- Record the lessons

Adapted from HSG159 Managing Contractors: A Guide for Employers, HSE, 2011 (www.hse.gov.uk/pubns/priced/hsg159.pdf)

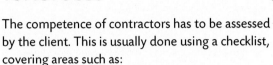

TOPIC FOCUS

The competence of contractors has to be assessed by the client. This is usually done using a checklist, covering areas such as:

- Are they experienced in the type of oil or gas process work to be carried out?
- Are they experienced and trained in offshore safety requirements?
- Are a suitable health and safety policy, organisation and arrangements in place?
- What is the quality and extent of their risk assessments?
- What is their recent health and safety performance (number of accidents, etc.)?
- Has any enforcement action been taken against them?
- Do they provide suitable, up-to-date method statements?
- Do they monitor health and safety and carry out site inspections?
- What are the qualifications and skills that they bring to the project?
- Do their workers carry a suitable skills card?
- Are they members of a professional body or trade association?
- Do they have employers' liability and public liability insurance?
- Do you have any references from previous clients?
- How do they appraise and select sub-contractors?
- What are their client liaison arrangements?

The installation owner or operator may choose not to use a contractor who cannot meet these requirements, and exclude one from future lists if their performance is seen to be poor.

Step 1 – Planning

Determine the work that is to be carried out by the contractors and look at how it can be carried out safely. This will require hazard identification and an assessment of the risks involved, both to contractors' workers and your directly employed installation workers. Establish what the likelihood is of anything going wrong, and, if it does, how serious it will be. From this you can, together with the contractor, determine the risk controls needed. This may include the use of formal permit-to-work systems, which will help safeguard contractors and your own workers on site.

Contractors' responsibilities include the provision of their own risk assessment, which should fit in with yours. This will confirm the adequacy of your own risk assessment and provide you with information on how the contractor can be expected to perform. The contractor will also be expected to fully adhere to the requirements of any permit-to-work system they are working under.

Step 2 – Choosing a Contractor

The Topic Focus above highlights the information you need to determine the competence and suitability of the contractor for a particular project. In some cases, the contractor may already be known to you, or may have carried out work for you in the past. Selection of contractors should not be based on cost alone – use all criteria (cost, experience, availability, reliability, and their health and safety records and performance).

You also need to decide whether to allow your selected contractor to sub-contract work himself. This can cause all sorts of problems, and needs very close management and agreed rules beforehand.

Step 3 – Contractors Working on Site

Contractors should go through the company health and safety and other induction programmes and, if working offshore, all necessary escape, evacuation and rescue training that directly employed workers have. Their work programmes (onshore and off) should be managed to the extent that they have an attendance control system the same as directly employed workers, and while on-site their whereabouts is known at all times.

A site contact should be established who can liaise with the contractors on a routine basis, and pass on all information about the project they are involved with (job changes, programme changes, timing, etc.). The purpose here is not to **control** the job but to ensure that the contractor does.

Step 4 – Keeping a Check

Remember, the intention is to ensure that the contractor has full control of their work, not to control it for them. The amount of contact is important: not enough and you are likely to miss essentials, too much and you are in the way. The best way is to establish a plan, and meet regularly to monitor its progress. Make sure all safe systems of work (method statements, permits-to-work, etc.) are closely followed, and that all incidents are reported and investigated.

Step 5 – Reviewing the Work

The job is not finished when the contractor says so, but when you mutually agree, after rigorous checks, that it is concluded to your satisfaction. You must evaluate the standard and quality of the contractor's work, their ability to follow the plan, meet deadlines, etc., and the safety of their performance throughout. Punch lists are produced on completion of contracted work and before handover of equipment to ensure that the equipment has been accepted by the company, particularly where problems may still exist.

Record the contractor's performance (it may help with your next contractor selection) and note any lessons learned from this experience in a record of the review.

Meet regularly with contractors to monitor progress

MORE...

If you wish to look at further guidance on managing contractors you can refer to the UK HSE's publication HSG159, *Managing Contractors: A Guide for Employers*, which you can access at:

www.hse.gov.uk

Remember that this is a UK publication and may refer to Regulations that do not apply in other countries.

Contractor Management

SAFE HANDOVER – UNDERSTANDING THE HAZARDS

We will look in more detail at shift handovers later, but be aware that the process of changing from one operational team (shift) to another can have significant problems, especially where 12-hour shifts operate. There will be issues such as:

- Not enough time allowed for shift handover.
- No formal shift handover meetings held.
- Off-going/on-coming members failing to attend shift handover meeting.
- Outgoing shift wanting to get off.
- Incoming shift seeing problems ahead and wanting to get on with them.
- Conflict between the shifts (how much the off-going shift actually achieved, etc).
- A tendency for the off-going shift to leave work they don't want to do.
- Failure to meet face-to-face to discuss the issues.
- Failure to use adequate written communication.
- Not keeping good shift records.
- Off-going shift failing to hand over records, or leaving things out.
- No continuation between parties to ensure permits-to-work are handed over properly.
- Lack of continuity with contractors.

REVISION QUESTIONS

1. What four factors must we consider to ensure that the work that contractors do is covered by our own usual methods of safe working, to prevent accidents?

2. Identify the simple "Five Steps" used to manage contractors.

(Suggested Answers are at the end.)

Process Safety Management (PSM)

> ## KEY INFORMATION
>
> Controls available in process safety management include:
>
> - Spacing of operating plant.
> - Positioning and protection of control rooms and critical equipment, specifically occupied buildings assessment, temporary refuge (offshore) and the critical safety systems associated with temporary refuge integrity (fire resistance, blast resistance, heating, ventilation and air conditioning, access to evacuation means, etc.).
>
> Management of change has controls that include:
>
> - Risk assessment and authorisation of changes by competent persons.

The process industry uses the **Dow Fire and Explosion Hazard Index** (Dow Chemicals 1964) and the **Mond Fire and Explosion and Toxicity Index** (ICI, 1979), which deal with fire and explosion hazard-rating of process plant. The Dow and Mond indices are rapid hazard assessment methods for use on chemical plant during process and plant development, and in the design of plant layout.

The Dow Fire and Explosion Index is probably the most frequently used method to evaluate hazards of fire and explosion in plant and installations. It divides plant into units and calculates the hazards in each unit from chemical substances.

Both indices give a realistic value to the risk of each individual process unit due to potential fires and explosion. Issues such as facilities handling and the storage of flammable liquids show up a potential fire risk. Fires associated with flammable liquids can be pool fires, jet fires, flash fires, or boiling-liquid expanding-vapour explosions (BLEVEs). The potential for these events depends on the type of containment, the type of release that may occur and the available sources of ignition.

Fire-hazard analysis should identify separate hazards and determine suitable preventive measures where losses could occur from events such as:

- The concentration of combustible materials (both in storage and in use).
- The configuration of combustible materials, buildings, furnishings, etc. that allow fire spread.
- Exposure to fire, heat, smoke, steam, etc, which may require areas to be evacuated for safety functions.
- Fires occurring in control rooms or other safety-critical areas.
- Lack of (or poor) access, which could affect fire-fighting in safety-critical areas.
- Lack of (or poor) smoke removal or control in safety-critical areas.
- Lack of explosion prevention or relief measures.
- Failure or loss of electrical supplies.
- Inadvertent operation of fire-suppression systems.

The fire analysis must consider a fire spreading from one unit to another, so work should progress in stages, starting with simple scenarios and moving to the more detailed fire potential later in the analysis.

The analysis will allow designers and engineers to minimise the potential for fire on the installation at an early stage. The mitigations used can include:

- Limiting any inventories of flammable or combustible materials to an absolute minimum.
- Separating redundant safety-related units so that one fire cannot affect all units in operation (e.g. storage vessel, item of plant, drilling floor, unloading facility).
- Isolating critical areas from non-critical areas so that a single fire in a non-critical area cannot adversely affect performance or operation in any other areas.
- Implementing administrative management systems and procedures to control hazardous operations and the introduction of flammable and combustible materials.

Process Safety Management (PSM)

MANAGEMENT OF CHANGE CONTROLS

Formal written procedures should be put in place that ensure all changes to process systems are assessed for the impact the changes will have on safe process operation. Some of the changes will require formal change control, whereas others may already have been evaluated to determine if there will be an increased level of risk associated with the change, which may have been built in to the original design and is accounted for in normal operating procedures.

Suitable arrangements must be put in place to ensure the effective management of changes to process systems. Procedures must identify the scope of the changes, the roles and responsibilities of those managing and making the changes, how risk analysis is to be undertaken, and methods to be used to communicate the changes to, and train, personnel involved.

When making hardware or software modifications, all changes that are not already part of the process system design should undergo change control, taking into account the plant design limits, allowable modes of operation, control and safety system settings. Documentation that may be involved in the evaluation includes:

- Original process system designs (basis for design).
- Process flow diagrams.
- Cause and effect diagrams.
- List of control, alarm and trip settings.
- Process equipment specifications.
- Mechanical equipment specifications.
- Drawings detailing classification of hazardous areas.
- Line list.

For temporary changes to process systems, such as the use of an override, or inhibit on a safety-related system, control can be effected through a separate procedure covering this, but must be kept under review in the change procedure.

Change control will be required when equipment is replaced with non-identical parts, or when new items of equipment are added to the system whether they are for safety-related purposes or not.

Change control will be needed if changes are made to the operating procedures, unless they take place within an established design basis and safe operating envelope (see later in Element 3).

Roles and Responsibilities – Making the Change

When making changes in line management and functional responsibilities, gaps can be prevented by careful mapping of the organisational changes. Personnel and their skills must be matched to the requirements of the task. This will identify the need for further training, and it is useful to phase the changes in (rather than do it in one change) to ensure transfer is made safely and the competence of operators is matched to the level and phase of the change.

The UK HSE *Loss of Containment Manual*, originally published to help inspectors, suggests that the opportunity for initiating changes should be widely available to people associated with process systems. It should be done by using a purpose-designed change-proposal document that gives a full description of the proposed change, the date the proposal is made, and the reasons supporting the change, including all health, safety and welfare issues.

The proposal document should clearly identify those persons who can authorise different types of change, and should involve personnel with suitable backgrounds and experience to make sure that changes will not result in operations outside established safe limits, e.g. if changes are proposed for an offshore installation, onshore guidance may be necessary.

Good monitoring needs to ensure that application of the procedures is not short-circuited, nor any of the elements missed out. Independent auditing of safety management systems should take place, with good communication and feedback, particularly where proposals for change are not approved.

> **REVISION QUESTION**
>
> 3. What is the Dow Fire and Explosion Index?
> (Suggested Answers are at the end.)

Permit-to-Work Procedures

ROLE AND PURPOSE OF A PERMIT-TO-WORK SYSTEM

Permit-to-work procedures are used to ensure that non-routine, usually hazardous work is assessed, planned, authorised and carried out in such a way as to ensure the health and safety of the workers involved, and others who may be affected. It ensures that proper consideration is given to the risks and that they are dealt with before the task starts and throughout the duration of the ongoing work. Equally important is controlling the completion of the work.

Permits-to-work detail and explain:

- The work involved.
- What isolations are required.
- Hazards in the work to be carried out.
- Precautions to avoid injury.

In addition:

- The persons (representatives of the company) requiring work to be carried out under a permit-to-work will be known as the **Originator** (permit originator).
- The permit-to-work is usually issued by a person known as the **Issuing Authority**.
- All persons using a permit-to-work system (Permit Users) need to be **trained** in its correct use and any emergency procedures required by the permit.
- The permit must be **signed** by the issuing authority and the person in charge of those carrying out the work (or somebody who is responsible for the work).

- A number of different copies are required:
    - One retained at the work site.
    - One retained by the competent, authorised person (permit applicant).
    - One kept at a permit control office (where lock-off keys may be kept during the work to prevent de-isolation of the equipment being worked on) by the permit signatory.
- If the work is to be continued by another worker or team of workers, the permit must be endorsed by them before transfer of the work to them.
- On completion of the work, the permit is returned for cancellation following de-isolation before return to service.
- Permits-to-work should be audited and inspected at regular intervals to ensure the validity of the procedures in place and that the documents and records kept are completed accurately.

Lloyds Register and DNV (Det Norske Veritas, Norway) are two companies that offer auditing, certification and verification of systems such as permits-to-work, as well as OHSAS 18001 safety management systems and SCC (Safety Checklists for Contractors).

Permit-to-Work Procedures

KEY FEATURES OF A PERMIT-TO-WORK

TOPIC FOCUS

A typical electrical permit-to-work has a number of elements, e.g.

- Title and permit number.
- Reference to other permits/isolation certificates in place.
- Equipment, distribution board, circuit or job location, and plant identification.
- Description and nature of the electrical work to be carried out.
- Hazards identified and precautions necessary.
- Protective equipment and PPE required.
- Authorisation that it's safe to work.
- Date, time and duration of the permit.
- Identification of workers in control of the work.
- Permit acceptance – by those doing the work.
- Considerations for extending the terms of the permit.
- Returning to service on completion of the work.
- Cancellation certifying that testing has been carried out and the plant satisfactorily re-commissioned.

Authorised/Competent Persons Using Permits-to-Work

An issuing authority will issue permits to work to the performing authority (see table later).

The **Issuing Authority** should:

- Be in control of the working conditions and potential hazards.
- Be competent and trained in the permit-issuing procedures to ensure that all health and safety precautions are identified and observed.
- Be authorised and appointed in writing by the installation owner or operator to issue permits-to-work.
- **Not** be the same person as the permit user.

The **issuing authority** may also be the **manager** or **competent person appointing contractors**. Their responsibilities will include ensuring:

- All who may be affected by the work have been informed.
- The work area has been inspected before work begins.
- All hazards have been identified.
- All health and safety precautions have been defined. This may involve consultation with installation specialists for certain tasks (electrical expert, engineer, etc).
- Any necessary tests have been completed.
- Permit conditions are established.
- The permit is completed with the permit user.
- The precautions specified in the permit are in place before work starts.
- Change-over (handover) procedures are followed, as appropriate.
- The permit is accepted and signed for by the permit applicant.
- All conditions of the permit are maintained throughout the work.
- The hand-back procedure is implemented.

The **Performing Authority** should be:

- In control of the work to be done; and/or
- Responsible for carrying out the work.

Their responsibilities will include:

- Ensuring that the nature of the work and the potential hazards are fully understood by all persons carrying out the permit task.
- Complying with the health and safety precautions specified in the permit.
- Ensuring that only work authorised by the permit is carried out.
- Ensuring that the work is confined within the area specified in the permit.
- Remaining in direct supervision of the work at all times.
- Ensuring that the permit user is informed should the task have to be passed over (handed over) to another person.
- Ensuring that the area and equipment are brought back to their operational condition on completion of the work.
- Ensuring that the hand-back procedure is complete.

Extension/Shift Handover Procedures

If a **permit user** needs to leave a task part-way through, or before completion of the permit's validity and pass the task to another permit user, then the extension/handover section of the permit must be completed with the issuing authority before any change takes place (e.g. at shift changes, etc).

Under no circumstances must the task be continued by other persons until this has been completed and the issuing authority is satisfied that the new permit user is familiar with the hazards and the risks associated with the work, and that the suitable controls and preventive measures are (or remain) in place.

In the event of the **issuing authority** needing to change while the permit is open, the change-over section of the permit must be completed. Re-establishing the terms of the permit is not necessary providing the existing issuing authority fully hands over briefs to the new issuing authority.

TYPES OF PERMITS-TO-WORK

Separate permits are required for **different tasks**, e.g.

- Hot work (welding, burning, grinding, etc.).
- Live or high-voltage work.
- Working at height.
- Working over water.
- Work in confined spaces.
- Special permits for work carried out under special conditions (usually maintenance work of a non-routine nature).

Records of all new and completed permits must be kept.

We will look at hot-work permits in more detail later in this element.

Comparison of Titles for Roles Within Permit-to-Work Systems

Role	Suggested Title	Alternative Titles
Person requiring the job to be done	Originator	Permit originator, requestor
Person working under the terms of the permit	Permit user	Competent person
Person authorising the permit for issue, e.g. if an extra level of authorisation is required*	Permit authoriser	OIM (Offshore Installation Manager), approver
Person issuing the permit	Issuing authority	Responsible person, permit coordinator, asset shift supervisor, permit issuer
Person accepting the permit on behalf of the permit user(s)	Performing authority	Acceptor, nominated person, work leader, person in charge of the work
Person in control of the location where the work is to be carried out	Area authority	Nominated area operator, responsible person, system operator
Person carrying out checks as detailed on the permit	Site checker	Gas tester, authorised gas tester
Person responsible for making isolations	Isolating authority	Authorised person (electrical, mechanical, process), responsible person (e.g. responsible electrical person, or electrical responsible person)

*Where the potential for harm is considered to be particularly high, the permit should be seen by a second person (the permit authoriser) before issue, i.e. the authorisation procedure should be more rigorous. In any case, a person should not issue a permit to him or herself.

Adapted from HSG250 Guidance on Permit-to-Work Systems – A Guide for the Petroleum, Chemical and Allied Industries, HSE, 2005 (www.hse.gov.uk/pubns/priced/hsg250.pdf)

Permit-to-Work Procedures

	PERMIT-TO-WORK
1.	**PERMIT TITLE**
2.	**PERMIT REFERENCE NUMBER** Reference to other relevant permits or isolation certificates can be referenced here.
3	**JOB LOCATION**
4.	**PLANT OR EQUIPMENT IDENTIFICATION**
5.	**DESCRIPTION OF THE WORK TO BE DONE AND ITS LIMITATIONS**
6.	**HAZARD IDENTIFICATION** Including residual hazards and hazards associated with the work.
7.	**PRECAUTIONS NECESSARY AND ACTIONS IN THE EVENT OF AN EMERGENCY** People who carry out precautions, e.g. isolating authority, should sign that precautions have been taken.
8.	**PROTECTIVE EQUIPMENT REQUIRED (INCLUDING PPE)**
9.	**PERMIT ISSUE** Signature (of issuing authority) confirming that isolations have been made and precautions taken, except where these can only be taken during the work. Date and time duration of the permit is indicated here. In the case of major hazard/high-risk work, a further signature from the permit authoriser will be needed.
10.	**PERMIT ACCEPTANCE** Signature confirming understanding of work to be done, hazards involved and precautions required. Also confirming permit information has been explained to all workers involved.
11.	**EXTENSION/SHIFT HANDOVER PROCEDURES** Signatures confirming checks have been made that plant remains safe to be worked on, and new performing authorities and permit users have been made fully aware of the hazards and precautions. New expiry time given.
12.	**HAND-BACK** Signed by performing authority certifying that work is complete. Signed by issuing authority certifying work completed and plant ready for testing and recommissioning.
13.	**PERMIT CANCELLATION** Certifying work tested and plant satisfactorily recommissioned.

Example of a permit-to-work certificate showing the basic elements (Adapted from HSG250 Guidance on Permit-to-Work Systems – A Guide for the Petroleum, Chemical and Allied Industries, HSE, 2005 (www.hse.gov.uk/pubns/priced/hsg250.pdf)

As noted in the table above, where the potential for harm is considered to be particularly high, the permit should be seen by a second person (the permit authoriser) before issue, i.e. the authorisation procedure should be more rigorous.

INTERFACES WITH ADJACENT PLANT

At the time that permits-to-work are issued it is important that considerations are made for all other plant and equipment on the installation. What must be prevented is a permit being issued to shut down one item of plant when another, exactly the same, is already shut down for work. This is vital for safety-critical plant. The Piper Alpha disaster showed us that, owing to a breakdown on one item of plant, another was required to come online, but couldn't, because a valve had been removed from that one during other work, leaving two unserviceable units.

INTERFACES WITH CONTRACTORS

We have already seen that contractors have responsibilities to carry out their own risk assessments and, in some cases, work under the controls of a permit-to-work. For continuity, contractors should be regarded in exactly the same way as directly employed workers for the purpose of the permit-to-work system. Note that they will only be a permit user; only the manager appointing them will be allowed to act as the issuing authority.

SAFE ISOLATION, LOCK-OUT AND TAG-OUT SYSTEMS

Although safeguards are provided that prevent access to dangerous or moving parts of machinery during normal operations, they may not be effective at all times because of the need to gain access to hazardous areas, e.g. to clean or carry out maintenance or setting, adjustments or repairs. This is particularly important with regard to work on live electrical circuits and components. Strict controls and safeguards need to be put in place to prevent injury in such circumstances.

The principal requirements will be the removal (isolation) of energy sources, a method of prevention of accidental re-application of the energy source, and adequate warnings and safeguards for those at work on isolated equipment and machinery.

Lock-out/tag-out systems provide warnings and safeguards

These systems are concerned with the safe isolation of:

- Electrical supplies.
- Hydraulic (oil) power.
- Pneumatic power and stored energy.
- Residual energy.
- Combustion engines.
- Natural gravitational forces weight.
- Steam or high-pressure water systems.
- Any combinations of, or additions to the above.

> ### GLOSSARY
>
> **SAFE ISOLATION**
> The interruption, disconnection and separation of all the equipment's motive power sources in such a way that this disconnection and separation is *secure by lockable means.*

An isolation system provides safe access onto and into plant and machinery that may have fixed or removable guards, interlocked safety control systems and various sources of energy, such as electrical circuits and equipment. Safe isolation is required whenever accidental or inadvertent operation or energising of plant or machinery electrical or power systems could cause injury.

Live working on electrical circuits and equipment is strictly limited to qualified electricians, and then only with properly insulated test equipment for the purpose of fault finding. Connection or disconnection is not permitted on any live circuits.

Procedures and Standards

SAFE ISOLATION STEPS

(a) Machinery or plant that is to be worked on with power isolated is to be stopped by normal means.

(b) All residual energy reserves, be they pneumatic, hydraulic, electric, etc. are to be exhausted/discharged.

(c) All moving parts must be stopped in a safe position that is also suitable for the work to be carried out.

(d) The electrical main isolator(s) must be turned "OFF". This is the primary means of isolation on most plant and equipment.

(e) A padlock is to be fitted to the isolator to secure it in the off position. Locks should ideally be labelled or coded to identify the owner of the lock.

Emergency stop buttons with integral locks normally only lockout the control circuitry and therefore are **not suitable** for access into dangerous areas. Access into dangerous areas should only be carried out with the main isolator locked off.

Permit-to-Work Procedures

LOCK-OUT/TAG-OUT SYSTEMS

Where multiple isolator lock-off is required to achieve safe isolation, this must be documented locally as a safe system of work.

(f) Where more than one person may require access during isolation, a **safety clamp** (e.g. Itex type) should be fitted to the main isolator. This will accept a number of separate padlocks, which should be fitted and locked into the clamp as required. Each person should retain the key for their own lock.

(g) An appropriate **warning notice** is to be posted on the normal means of stopping/starting the machine and/or the mains isolator.

(h) Captive key systems should only be considered as a secondary means of isolation.

Note: Some systems enable an isolation that results in a total break of the power supply (415V) while others only isolate the control circuits (110V). Workers must therefore ensure that the 415V supply is dead before entering such guarded areas. This should be achieved on all such tasks by electrical isolation as in steps (d), (e) and (f) above.

(i) Where **total separation** from an electricity supply is the only positive means of isolation, a qualified maintenance engineer or electrician should remove the fuses from the power supply. He must lock the fuse box, put a suitable warning notice on the machine to advise that the fuses are removed, and put the fuses in a safe place, identifying on them where they are taken from.

(j) Where other energy sources (e.g. pressurised gases or liquids in pipelines or pressure systems) are also involved it may be necessary to disconnect hoses or pipes and to fit suitable blanks. Blanks, valve taps, etc. should be locked in place wherever possible, and suitable (and visible) warning notices fitted.

(k) Where necessary, physical restraints should be fitted to prevent movement or "fall" of machinery parts after isolation of the power supply and disconnection of the energy source (e.g. pegging, locking, propping).

(l) Before any work is carried out on plant or equipment driven by combustion engines (e.g. generators or pumps) the engine must be stopped by normal means and the electrical supply to the engine physically disconnected.

(m) Local management should make lock control arrangements to control shift change-over. Such arrangements must control the potential of locks being removed at the end of the shifts with safeguards left removed.

(n) **Safe isolation must always be proven before commencing the work to be done** (prove the system is "dead").

(o) Where work is carried out under the controls of a permit-to-work, ensure that all appropriate precautions required by the permit are followed and recorded as necessary.

RE-CONNECTION PROCEDURE

(a) Each person is to ensure that all items and tools used are correctly put away, and items removed are correctly refitted.

(b) Only the person fitting a padlock must unlock and remove it. Local management is to make alternative lock control arrangements to control shift change-over.

(c) Only the person putting in place a warning notice is to remove it.

(d) Once all padlocks, safety clamps and warning notices have been removed, checks are to be carried out by the person who first carried out the isolation to ensure that it is safe to re-connect the energy source(s).

In addition, the person/operator who will re-start a machine is to carry out their own final checks that the machine is in a safe condition to re-start, e.g.

– All padlocks removed.

– All warning notices removed.

– All persons are in a safe position away from moving parts.

Training and Competence

Permit-to-work systems require continual use so that risk awareness and enhanced safety performance of the workforce are assured. Initial and continuous training are required to improve understanding of the systems and give ownership to those who use them. This should be done for all workers at all levels in the organisation who use permits-to-work.

> ## REVISION QUESTIONS
>
> 4. What are the four main areas detailed and explained in a permit-to-work?
>
> 5. Identify six types of work where a permit-to-work might be required.
>
> 6. Identify four areas other than electricity where a safe isolation procedure might be used.
>
> 7. Explain the meaning of the term 'safe isolation'.
>
> (Suggested Answers are at the end.)

Key Principles of Safe Shift Handover

KEY INFORMATION

- A shift handover is a critical time for passing on information about the status of operations.
- Shift handover should be:
  - High priority, and conducted face-to-face.
  - Two-way, with both sets of participants taking responsibility for its effectiveness.
  - Carried out using verbal and written communication, with emphasis given to written communication.
  - Based on analysis of the information needs of the oncoming shift staff.
  - Given as much time as is necessary.

SAFETY-CRITICAL COMMUNICATIONS

Companies use many different methods of communication, but few really understand how communications can affect safety. Methods of getting the message across include:

- General communications – signs, notices, posters, and general non-verbal methods.
- Verbal systems messages, such as public-address announcements.
- Safety meeting minutes and records.
- Job-specific communications, tool-box talks, system briefs and de-briefs, shift handovers.
- Informal communications, where general discussions include safety issues.
- Emergency communications – alarms, PA announcements, briefings, communicating with emergency and rescue services.

Failure is often blamed on *"a lack of communications"*, but it is probably more true to say it is due to *"the wrong type of communication"*, or *"a breakdown in communications"*.

Safety-critical communications to consider are:

- Shift handover.
- Emergency communications.
- Remote communication, e.g. between control room and outside operators.
- Permit-to-work procedures.
- Informing contractors of hazards and risks.
- Using radios and personal communicators, e.g. pagers, mobile phones.
- Marking and labelling of plant for identification.
- Informing about procedural changes.

The most critical communication time is often considered to be the **shift handover**, where one group has just completed a 12-hour shift and hands over operations to a new group just beginning their shift. This can be made more critical when serious events or breakdowns have occurred during the departing shift period, and often involves communication between different teams, such as production and maintenance.

Unreliable communications may be due to:

- Missed or missing information.
- Inclusion of unnecessary information, causing confusion.
- Inaccurate or misleading information.
- Poor-quality information.
- Information not being understood (either by the transmitter or the receiver).
- Information not being carried forward over successive shifts.

These faults are more likely to occur when those passing the information on have a different understanding of the issues being communicated, or have different priorities. Often, the time available to communicate is deliberately cut short, especially by those going off shift.

Effective communications may be assured by:

- Knowing and carefully specifying the key information to be communicated.
- Not transmitting unnecessary information.
- Using records and aids to confirm accuracy, such as computer displays, log books, etc.
- Repeating information by using both verbal and written methods (read the message to them).
- Not hurrying to get away – allowing time to communicate the message and for it to be accepted and understood.
- Effective two-way communication – ensuring that both the giver and receiver of information give and understand accurately.
- Having both parties continually confirm the message; repeating it for clarification.
- Encouraging face-to-face communication as much as possible.
- Training all workers (and contractors, where necessary) in good communication skills.
- Setting your own (high) company communication standards.

Key Principles of Safe Shift Handover

SHIFT HANDOVER

This is a situation when communication is critical, so shift handovers must be handled well. Most problems in communication occur:

- During plant maintenance, when it runs across more than one shift. Wherever possible, plan to have maintenance work completed within one shift, cutting out the risk of change-over miscommunication.
- In areas where safety systems may have been over-ridden (e.g. fire deluge system switched to manual).
- During deviations from normal working, such as breakdowns, or lack of spares.
- When members of the team have been absent from work for long periods.
- If handover takes place between experienced and inexperienced staff.

Effective communication is essential – especially at shift handover

TOPIC FOCUS

To make handovers more effective:

- Make communication effectiveness at shift change-over a high priority.
- Include communication skills in the selection criteria for shift workers and train all staff to communicate well.
- Provide effective shift change-over procedures and train all shift workers to follow them.
- Conduct handovers face-to-face, with staff from both shifts taking part.
- Ensure both parties (on-coming and off-going crews) take joint responsibility for making all information accurate, using both verbal and written communication.

- Place an emphasis on written communication.
- Base all information communicated at handover on a pre-determined analysis of what detail the incoming shift needs to have.
- Ensure good operator support, by the use of shift-logs, maintenance records, information displays, all based on operators' needs.
- Take ideas for required information and effective information transfer from the shift teams – they can then ensure they get the information they need.
- Allow as much time as is necessary to ensure that communication is accurate and understood.

TOPIC FOCUS

The main operational issues communicated at shift hand-over include:

- Operational status of the installation or process.
- Maintenance operations carried out and completed.
- Maintenance issues begun but not completed.
- Clearance of permits-to-work.
- Hand-over of permits-to-work still open.
- Situations where safety systems have been overridden (e.g. fire deluge system switched to manual operation).
- Deviations from normal working, such as breakdowns, lack of spare parts, replacement equipment.
- Emergencies that occurred during the shift.
- Incidents or injuries following accidents during the shift.
- Operational issues that will occur in the on-coming shift.
- Maintenance operations planned during the on-coming shift.
- Events (drills or exercises) planned during the on-coming shift.

REVISION QUESTIONS

8. What five key principles should be employed to ensure a safe shift handover?
9. Identify four causes of ineffective communications.
10. When are problems in communications most likely to occur?

(Suggested Answers are at the end.)

Plant Operations and Maintenance

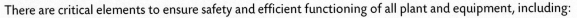

ASSET INTEGRITY

Asset integrity is all about the ability of an asset (drill platform, compressor, water pump, etc.) to carry out its intended function effectively and efficiently over its planned lifecycle, at the same time safeguarding the health and safety of those exposed to it and the operating environment.

Asset integrity management is how we ensure that people, systems, processes and resources that deliver the integrity of the asset are put in place, used and remain effective over the asset's lifecycle. These are **Asset Integrity Management Systems (AIMS)**.

The lifecycle of any asset follows six suggested stages; the objectives, deliverables and activities considered fundamental to assuring asset integrity are as follows:

1. LIFECYCLE PHASE: DESIGN

Objectives: Design installation to achieve optimal integrity performance throughout the lifecycle, ensuring optimum technical safe solution, and that all lifecycle aspects are considered.

- Deliverables/activities:
  - Safety studies.
  - Design, maintenance and inspection, operating, Manning and verification philosophies.
  - Maintenance and inspection strategy.
  - Operations strategy.
  - Create and document management systems.
  - Design review by verifier.

2. LIFECYCLE PHASE: CONSTRUCTION AND HOOK-UP

Objectives: Construct in accordance with design, and through Quality planning process confirm delivery up to and including 'mechanical completion'.

- Deliverables/activities:
  - Procurement quality plans.
  - Inspection/testing records.
  - Document completion and handover.
  - Verification/suitability status.

3. LIFECYCLE PHASE: COMMISSIONING

Objectives: Demonstrate through function testing and acceptance that design specification has been achieved and that Performance Standards are being met.

- Deliverables/activities:
  - Commission and function-test against design specification and Performance Standards.
  - Commissioning completion packages and sign off.
  - Verification (ICP (independent and competent person)).
  - Handover to operation.

4. LIFECYCLE PHASE: OPERATIONS

Objectives: Operate plant within design limits. Implement and monitor management systems.

- Deliverables/activities:
  - Ongoing evaluation of integrity risks.
  - Assurance process.
  - Maintain and inspect plant.
  - Monitoring of mitigation controls.
  - Verification (ICP).

5. LIFECYCLE PHASE: MODIFICATIONS

Objectives: Control changes to asset and/or operation.

- Deliverables/activities:
  - Change management process (including design, construct new equipment/facilities and management of redundant plant and equipment).
  - Assure and verify changes.

6. LIFECYCLE PHASE: DE-COMMISSIONING

Objectives: Remove from service entire installation.

- Deliverables/activities:
  - Safety Studies.
  - De-commissioning philosophies.
  - De-commissioning strategy.
  - De-commissioning plan.

Source: adapted from Asset Integrity Toolkit, © 2006 UK Offshore Operators Association (www.stepchangeinsafety.net/knowledgecentre/publications/publication.cfm/publicationid/10)

Inspection

At the heart of good maintenance is a thorough programme of regular inspection. This should cover every safety-critical element (SCE) of the assets, and all maintenance and inspection tasks for each SCE should be clearly defined. Close monitoring of inspections can lead to either an increase or decrease in the inspection intervals, depending on the findings.

Inspection will be required in a number of different circumstances, including:

After installation or re-installation	Before being used for the first time or after refitting, to prevent faults from incorrect installation.
Where deterioration leads to a significant risk	E.g. items of equipment left out in all weathers, or in a harsh (perhaps exposed to chemicals) environment.
Where exceptional circumstances may jeopardise safety	E.g. after major modifications or repair, known or suspected damage, change of use or after long periods of disuse.

Some inspections will be required by national or local regulations, such as those for lifting equipment, pressure vessels, compressed-air systems, boilers, pipelines, local exhaust ventilation systems, etc.

Inspection of the integrity of a pipeline

Testing

As part of the maintenance programme, assets may undergo testing to ensure they match required performance criteria, and when they are returned to operation should undergo functional testing within the total system. The same criteria as inspection may be applied, and again some testing procedures may be required under national or local regulations, such as:

- Pressure vessels (including pipelines) – in accordance with a written scheme of examination. Safety of pressure vessels: internal and external inspection and hydraulic testing every 10 years.
- Lifting equipment – six-monthly, if persons carried; 12 months for other, unless specified in written scheme by operator.

Maintenance

Assets should be maintained:

- In an efficient state.
- In efficient working order and in good repair, i.e. where a defect, damage or wear is detected, appropriate remedial action should be taken.

Routine checks and maintenance should be carried out to ensure that all equipment operates efficiently and effectively and remains in a safe condition. Where equipment has its own maintenance or running log, the log must be kept up to date.

Maintenance work should be:

- Only undertaken by competent people.
- Carried out without exposing maintenance workers to risks to their health and safety.

Maintenance should ensure all equipment functions efficiently and in a safe condition

Plant Operations and Maintenance

MAINTENANCE STRATEGIES

It is a legal requirement to provide and maintain safe plant and equipment. New equipment is expected to work well, but as it gets older it is likely to break down more often, develop more faults, give lower-quality output, slow down and generally wear. If this is allowed to continue, the performance of plant and machinery will decline until it becomes unsatisfactory. A way to avoid this is to have maintenance policies.

Ideally, maintenance work should be carried out when equipment is shut down, and maintenance on live or operating equipment should be avoided (if this is not possible, a permit-to-work may be required). Scheduling maintenance may involve:

- **Emergency/breakdown maintenance** – where breakdown or failure does not have a major effect on production or processes.
- **Opportunity maintenance** – using quiet 'downtime' to carry out maintenance, or using the opportunity when another item has failed and is undergoing maintenance.
- **Working adjustments** – occur regularly in the workplace while equipment is in operation, but failures have been identified (e.g. a bolt is loose and can be tightened with the plant running).
- **Running repairs** – used to get failed items of plant back running as soon as possible.
- **Servicing and inspection** – a strategy to minimise potential breakdowns, by looking for potential failures and taking remedial action before failure occurs.
- **Shutdown maintenance** – where a production or process is dependent on all equipment functioning and its loss would halt or seriously hinder the operation.
- **Planned preventive maintenance (PPM)** - this is monitored, and operated at regular calendar-based intervals, or on a time or running-hours basis.
- **Routine condition-monitoring** – usually of safety-critical parts, e.g. whenever a car is serviced, the remaining thickness of brake linings/shoes, and tyre-tread depth will be monitored.

Any maintenance strategy should reflect whether the equipment has a critical or central role. For example, if all production depends on a conveyor system moving a product from one location to another and if, without it, production stops, the maintenance strategy should ensure the minimum downtime during the production process.

Records should be kept of all maintenance, remedial actions taken, spare parts and materials used, etc.

TOPIC FOCUS

Planned preventive maintenance (PPM) should be applied where:

- The safety of an item of equipment or machinery depends on the installation conditions.
- An item of equipment or machinery is exposed to conditions that could cause dangerous deterioration.

The programme should be based on regular inspections of the equipment or machinery, and should be recorded.

Corrosion Prevention

The conditions that cause corrosion and the types of corrosion arise in different ways, and include:

- General wastage of material (uniform corrosion).
- Galvanic corrosion (dissimilar metals in contact).
- Pitting (localised attack).
- Intergranular corrosion.
- Stress corrosion.
- Erosion corrosion.
- Corrosion fatigue.
- High temperature oxidisation.
- Hydrogen embrittlement.

There are two main principles by which corrosion may be prevented or minimised: **surface coating** and **corrosion-resistant** materials.

In **surface coating**, a metallic surface can be insulated from the corrosive medium by a protective coating, which includes paints, varnishes, and metallic films, all having good corrosion resistance and artificially thickened oxide films. This may be useful against atmospheric corrosion.

Where corrosive action is severe, or where mechanical abrasion is likely to damage surface coatings, **metals or alloys having an inherent resistance to corrosion** can be used. These materials are more expensive, which can limit their use to chemical engineering and marine-engineering equipment.

The life of equipment subjected to corrosive environments can be extended by proper attention to design details. Equipment should be designed to drain freely and completely, and internal surfaces should be smooth and free from crevasses where corrosion products can accumulate.

GLOSSARY

CORROSION
Tendency of a metal to return to its natural state, often called oxidisation (generally true of ferrous metals).

PROTECTIVE COATINGS

A wide range of paints and other organic coatings are used for the protection of mild steel structures. Paints are used mainly for protection from atmospheric corrosion. Special chemically-resistant paints have been developed for use on chemical process equipment, where chlorinated rubber and epoxy-based paints are often used. In the application of paints and other coatings, good surface preparation is essential to ensure good adhesion of the film, or coating.

Protection can be given to materials by processes such as metallic coatings, oxide coatings or other non-metallic coatings:

- Metallic coatings:
  - Cladding is a base metal, sandwiched within protective metals, e.g. mild steel clad with stainless steel.
  - Hot-dipped metal coating, e.g. tin and zinc coatings, such as tin plate or galvanising.
  - Molten-metal spraying.
  - Electro-plating.
- Oxide coating:
  - Anodising.
  - Beryllium oxide coating.
- Non-metallic coatings:
  - Phosphating.
  - Chromating.
  - Electro-painting.

Cathodic protection can also be used, similar to that used on boats and ships, which can be expected to corrode nearer to the stern since the manganese bronze propellers are anodic and salt water acts as a simple electrolyte.

CORROSION-RESISTANT MATERIALS

In order to select the correct material for construction, the process environment to which the material will be exposed must be clearly defined. In addition to the main corrosive chemicals present, the following should be considered:

- Temperature.
- Pressure.
- pH.
- Presence of trace impurities.
- Amount of aeration.
- Steam velocity and agitation.
- Heat-transfer rates.

Corrosion guides can be used for the preliminary screening of materials that are likely to be suitable.

OFFSHORE SYSTEMS

Most offshore processing equipment addresses corrosion at the design stage by using carbon-manganese (C-Mn) steel (mainly for vessels and pipework). All offshore equipment and systems that contain sea water and injection water are at risk of corrosion, including internal parts of firewater systems. Testing of these systems and wash-down can result in damage from water getting into lagging and insulation materials.

Failures due to corrosion can result in hydrocarbon releases, loss of production, and higher costs for repairs and maintenance of the systems.

Recognised monitoring systems are used, such as ultrasonic non-destructive testing (NDT), to check the condition of internal corrosion and the integrity of installation structures. In pipeline systems, inhibitor chemicals are injected, and internal and external surfaces of vessels are coated with corrosion control inhibitors.

In production systems with high partial pressures of carbon dioxide, or using sulphide-containing fluids, the construction materials used are vital, with corrosion-resistant alloys often being used. These are common in the construction of downhole safety valves. Where installations use C-Mn steels, chemical treatments are more often used for corrosion inhibition and biological control.

Corrosion-control practice and procedures include:

- Selection of materials: steels, corrosion-resistant alloys, plastics.
- Chemical treatments: biocides and corrosion inhibitors.
- Surface coatings: metallic, non-metallic and paints/organic coatings.
- Cathodic protection: galvanising and impressed current.
- Process and environmental controls: control of through-put, dehumidification.
- Initial design: safe concept, engineering and detail reviews, lifecycle implications and corrosion risks.

Corrosion management requires various mitigation processes, including risk assessment and corrosion inspection systems. Risk assessment can be used to determine the most appropriate inspection method. Inspection and monitoring will include risk-based assessment of:

- The operating environment.
- The composition of produced fluids (and changes in them).
- Metal wastage.
- Pitting corrosion.
- Erosion corrosion.
- Cracking (environmental cracking).
- Assessment of the corrosivity of fluids.
- Development of biological activity.

Plant Operations and Maintenance

Three monitoring systems are:

- **Inline systems** - devices placed in the system that have to be removed for monitoring, such as corrosion (weight-loss) coupons, bio-studs, etc.
- **Online techniques** - using corrosion monitoring devices fixed in the system, or process equipment:
    - Electrical resistance probes.
    - Linear polarisation resistance probes.
    - Fixed ultrasonic probes.
    - Acoustic emission.
    - Condition monitoring equipment.
- **Offline monitoring** - requires inspection and non-destructive testing:
    - Visual inspection (e.g. dye penetrant).
    - Ultrasonics.
    - Radiography (X-ray, etc).
    - Pulse eddy current.

We looked at inspection criteria earlier, and for corrosion monitoring both planned preventive maintenance (time or running hours-based) and opportunity inspections have value.

Corrosion awareness is important for those not directly involved in maintenance or corrosion control, and everyone should:

- Be able to recognise signs of corrosion and damage to ensure early treatment.
- Understand why inspection and monitoring are necessary, and their benefits.
- Understand the effects and benefits of corrosion control measures.

Competency and Training

Asset integrity, maintenance and inspection rely on high levels of skill, knowledge and competence. Asset integrity managers must ensure that they and all their staff understand all performance standards for each safety-critical element included in the asset integrity management (AIM) plan.

Everyone whose work can affect safety-critical element integrity and performance must be able to demonstrate their competence, including all contractors, and onshore maintenance and technical support teams.

As well as safety-critical communication issues, there will also be some specific performance influencing factors (PIFs) relating to maintenance, inspection and testing, which include:

- Work planning.
- Supervision.
- Permit-to-work and isolation procedures.
- Task design.

Competence is required to avoid human errors in maintenance, which can usually be traced back to how maintenance is managed. Maintenance errors are typically "unsafe acts", which lead to near-misses and incidents causing injury, ill health, loss or damage. Systems need to be in place to ensure competence at all levels.

RISK-BASED MAINTENANCE AND INSPECTION

Risk-based maintenance and inspection needs a formal process to identify the items of plant and equipment that have a risk of degradation, breakdown or failure, usually due to the operating conditions. Once the critical items have been ranked in relation to their risk, the maintenance system should recognise the controls to eliminate, reduce or manage the risks. This is generally based on an estimation of the:

- Probability of equipment, plant, or component failure.
- Consequences of that failure, considering as a minimum operational, safety and environmental impacts.

Risk-based inspection schemes allow a plan for carrying out critical inspections, using the following approach:

- Ensure the risks are reduced to as low as reasonably practicable (ALARP).
- Optimise the inspection schedules.
- Inspect the most critical items of plant, equipment and components.
- Use the most appropriate inspection methods.

The most critical items of plant should be inspected regularly

TECHNIQUES, PRINCIPLES AND IMPORTANCE OF SAFE OPERATION PROCEDURES AND MAINTENANCE

Safe Operation

All activities that are reasonably foreseeable should be subject to safe systems of work – safe operation. These include activities onshore, and those on offshore installations, where there are additional implications for health and safety. Offshore installations have additional associated activities involving other vessels, such as supply, support and diving vessels, helicopter activities and floating storage units, which must be taken into account.

Safe operation requires planned activities, controlled timetables and full operational guidelines to be in place. These have to be supported by the controlled and regulated shift patterns of skilled operatives and technicians.

Standard Operation Procedures

These are the day-to-day procedures ("standards of performance") that control, as described above, the requirement that "normal" activities are conducted safely. They will include step-by-step procedures that cover activities such as:

- Start-up.
- Shift handover.
- Shut-down.
- Loading and unloading.
- Planned maintenance.
- Performance standards for operations.
- Performance standards for plant and equipment.
- Performance standards for structures.
- Performance standards for pipelines.
- Performance standards for handling chemicals and materials.
- Emergency plans.
- Permit-to-work systems.
- Safe isolation procedures.
- Training programmes and competence assurance.

Safe Maintenance

Earlier, we looked at the need for routine checks and maintenance to be carried out to ensure that all equipment operates efficiently and effectively and remains in a safe condition. However, maintenance activities can also expose those carrying out the work to risk, therefore all maintenance activities must be carefully planned in advance. Key precautions include:

- Risk assessment.
- The use of competent maintenance workers.
- Procedural measures, such as permit-to-work.
- Ensuring suitable means of access to the work area.
- Physical isolation of the equipment.

To illustrate some aspects of this, the following figure shows a pump used to move flammable, corrosive slurry. At some stage the pump will require maintenance to ensure its continued safe operation, and this activity needs to be planned in advance. In order to remove the pump from its pipeline the flow to and from the pump has to be isolated, therefore isolation valves A and B are fitted at the suction and discharge ends of the pump assembly. When the pump is stopped and the flow isolated, the pump and immediate pipework may still be under pressure, so a vent valve C is fitted to enable this pressure to be relieved. The pump at this stage will still be filled with flammable corrosive slurry, therefore drain valve D is required to allow the pump to be emptied. Since the slurry is flammable as well as corrosive, there may be a risk of generating an explosive atmosphere once containment is broken, so inerting (see later) may be an additional control measure required.

You can see that in order to carry out this activity safely all the risks to the maintenance worker have to be identified at the planning stage and controlled by a range of both technical and procedural measures.

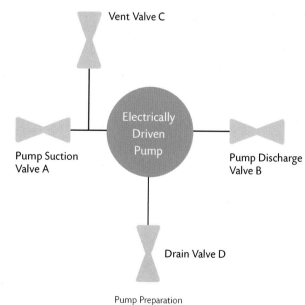

Pump Preparation

Plant Operations and Maintenance

CONTROL OF IGNITION SOURCES DURING MAINTENANCE AND OPERATIONS

There are many maintenance and operational activities that either create or are carried out in atmospheres that could be flammable or explosive. In such circumstances all ignition sources should be eliminated or adequately controlled.

TOPIC FOCUS

Fire Hazards and Precautions in Maintenance and Operations

- **Fire hazards:**
  - Hot work (welding, burning, cutting, soldering).
  - Use of flammable materials (solvents, gas cylinders, etc.).
  - Use of combustible materials (packaging, wrapping, filling materials).
  - Electrical work – especially on poorly maintained systems.
  - Use of defective portable electrical equipment including extension leads.
  - Overloading an electrical system used in the work and use of socket adaptors.
  - Workers smoking or burning rubbish on site.
- **Precautions:**
  - Use of hot-work permits.
  - Regular fire safety checks in the hot-work area (during and after work).
  - Use of burning/welding/soldering equipment only by qualified persons.
  - Consider fabrication of components off site.
  - Portable appliance testing and maintenance of electrical systems.
  - Proper control of flammable and combustible materials used or stored.
  - Regular removal of rubbish.
  - Prohibiting smoking.

Ignition Sources

Most fires in the workplace are caused by a lack of control over sources of ignition. Such fires are preventable by the use of carefully designed working systems and practices.

- **Electrical equipment** should be routinely inspected and tested to prevent faults that could cause sparks and overheating, which may not be noticed.
- **Hot work** such as welding and burning should be controlled with a permit-to-work when carried out in sensitive areas.
- **Smoking** should be controlled and limited to restricted areas on site (welfare areas).
- **Cooking and heating appliances** should be safely located (confined to a galley offshore) and used carefully. Gas supplies should have a master isolator valve clearly visible. They should not be left unattended.
- **Mechanical heat** (overheating) can be controlled by good maintenance programmes.
- **Deliberate ignition** (arson) should be prevented by good security, perimeter fences (onshore), CCTV and security lighting.

Welding

Welding (including flame-cutting and burning) involves many fire risks, both from gases used in the process and from electricity, which creates a high-energy spark or flame.

In circumstances where the flammable and combustible materials are the structure, materials or furnishings of the area, then, wherever possible, items should be removed to be welded in a dedicated safe area (workshop, etc).

Permit-to-Work Procedures

Welding, flame-cutting, use of blow lamps or soldering equipment, portable grinding equipment and even lead-lamps can pose a serious fire hazard through the production of sparks, heat or a naked flame.

These hazards must be controlled to prevent fires occurring, especially in areas where flammable materials, such as paint, timber, plastic, thinners, adhesives, etc. are stored or used, or where the production and storage processes may create flammable atmospheres. One method is to use a written permit-to-work system (see earlier) applicable to all workers involved, i.e. directly employed workers **and** contractors.

A **hot-work permit** ensures that:

- Formal arrangements are in place as a safe system of work.
- There is appropriate co-ordination with other people or activities to avoid any conflicts.
- Time limits are provided within which it is safe to carry out the work.
- Ignition sources (hot work) will not be introduced until combustible/flammable materials have been moved away from where the work is to be carried out.
- Fire-fighting measures are in place to tackle any fire that may occur.
- Specialised PPE, e.g. breathing apparatus, is provided.
- Appropriate methods of communication are used.

Further precautions for hot work in **confined spaces**:

- A confined-spaces permit may be required.
- Air monitoring may be necessary to determine air quality/ oxygen presence, and any hazardous conditions such as the presence of and amounts of gas or toxic residues, hydrocarbons, hydrogen sulphide, etc.
- Cylinders of flammable gases and oxygen should not be taken into confined spaces because of the risk of serious fire or explosion from a build-up of fuel gases, e.g. from a leak.
- All hot-work equipment (e.g. gas torch or arc electrode) should be removed from the confined space whenever work stops – even for a break.

Normal confined-spaces precautions required by such a permit-to-work will include the establishment of an **emergency plan**, which includes:

- Control of plant (shut-down, isolation, etc).
- Communication systems to persons on the outside.
- Communication systems with local services (offshore installation rescue teams, or onshore emergency services (by prior arrangement)).
- Rescue and resuscitation equipment (lifelines, lifting equipment).
- Additional sets of breathing apparatus.
- Provision of first aid.
- Fire-fighting precautions.
- Competency and training of rescue teams.

TOPIC FOCUS

Hot-Work Permit Requirements

A hot-work permit should contain the following details/precautions:

- Area safety inspection to ensure flammable materials removed from the work area or adequately protected from heat or sparks.
- Fire-fighting equipment to be available in the work area.
- Location and nature of work.
- Name of person in charge.
- Permitted time span of the activity and level of supervision required.
- Actions to be taken when the work is finished, including initial and subsequent checks that there are no smouldering or hot materials which could allow a fire to break out later.

Plant Operations and Maintenance

CLEANING AND GAS-FREEING

Cleaning and gas-freeing ("degassing") are processes applied to tanks and other vessels from time to time for various reasons, such as when changing from one product to another, or before entry into the vessel for inspection and maintenance purposes. In maintenance cases, the tank must not only be cleaned (to remove residues of product and contaminants) but must also be gas-free. Often, steam is used for both cleaning and gas-freeing, or gas-freeing is achieved by blowing fresh air (from portable air or water-powered air blowers) into the vessel.

Purging is the process of pumping an inert gas into the tank or vessel until hydrocarbons have been expelled, at least to below around 1%. This makes the vessel gas free for maintenance and inspection entry purposes.

Venting is opening all apertures in a tank or vessel and blowing air (either from a fan, or compressed air from cylinders or compressors) through the vessel to expel hydrocarbons and other gases. This can also be done through flexible trunking and even continued while persons are inside the tank or vessel to ensure the gas-free atmosphere remains while the work is carried out inside.

Offshore draining of water and product is normally done under process pressure to remove the contents, which are then washed out with sea water. It is sometimes achieved by the operation of collectors and drain valves in the tank and pipework systems. The contaminants are usually drained into a collector tank with a closed drain system (to prevent the escape of flammables) that incorporates a separator to remove the contaminants (which are collected and disposed of safely) leaving water to be disposed of to the drains (or into the sea offshore).

Oxygen and non-condensable (NCD) gases such as hydrogen, nitrogen and hydrocarbon gases again are drained through a collector and separator system that treats them before allowing safe discharge.

Inerting is a system used to make the atmosphere within a tank or vessel safe. It creates an atmosphere within the vessel in which hydrocarbon vapours cannot burn. The inert gas (nitrogen, nitrogen-enriched air, steam or carbon dioxide) increases the lower flammable limit while at the same time decreasing the upper flammable limit. With a total oxygen concentration in the vessel at around 11% (lower and upper flammability converged) the flammable range has gone, creating a safe atmosphere.

Inerting can be used to retain a safe atmosphere within an empty tank (usually after cleaning and gas-freeing), or as an inert gas (usually nitrogen) forming a blanket above a flammable product to prevent the emission of vapours, making the load safer to store and carry in this way.

Where any of the above work may require the entry of persons into tanks and vessels, the requirements of a **confined-space permit-to-work** should be followed.

TOPIC FOCUS

Hazards and precautions associated with maintenance activities:

- Hazardous substances:
  - Fuels.
  - Oils.
  - Greases.
  - Paints.
  - Cleaning solvents.
  - Acids.
  - Fibrous dust.
- Exposure to dangerous parts of machinery.
- Inadvertent start-up of machinery.
- Stored pressure or energy.
- Sharp shards of metal from broken parts contaminated with oil or grease.
- Collapse or fall of failed equipment.
- Restricted space, poor access, limited lighting and inadequate ventilation.
- Cold, wet, muddy conditions.
- Hot work (welding, grinding, burning):
  - Fire/explosion.
  - Noise.
  - Glare.
  - Heat.
  - Depletion of oxygen.

- Electrical tools:
  - Electrocution (inclement conditions).
  - Fire or explosion (flammable atmospheres).

Prevention measures might include:

- Suitable means of access.
- Physical isolation of the equipment.
- Portable lighting.
- Ventilation, including local exhaust ventilation.
- Use of suitable tools (substitute electrically-powered tools with pneumatic tools in certain environments).
- Not carrying out work in situ (removing items to be worked on to a more suitable location).
- Blocking or shoring up moving parts to prevent unexpected movement.
- Providing suitable protective equipment to reduce the effects of:
  - Hazardous substances.
  - Sharp objects.
  - Hot surfaces.

REVISION QUESTIONS

11. Identify four corrosion control practices and procedures.

12. Risk-based inspection schemes allow a plan for carrying out critical inspections. What four critical areas is this based on?

13. Identify four ignition sources that could arise from maintenance or operations on an installation.

(Suggested Answers are at the end.)

Start-Up and Shut-Down

ORGANISING, PLANNING AND CONTROLLING MAINTENANCE

Earlier, we noted the importance of maintenance and the problems that can be associated with it. Plant and equipment must be safely shut down before maintenance is carried out and started up safely on completion.

It is vital for the safety of maintenance personnel that all services are stopped, isolated, drained down, blanked, etc. and remain in a safe condition for the duration of the work. Much of this is ensured by the work being carried out under the controls of a permit-to-work. The permit will also have a completion section to ensure that all systems are put back into operable condition before start-up, to protect both maintenance and operations personnel.

This is especially important when maintenance is carried out on plant and equipment that process and store hydrocarbons. Emptying and draining of facilities must be assured so that all liquids, gases and residues are removed, leaving the plant safe to work on.

Good supervision and monitoring of activities is essential to ensure safe conditions throughout the duration of the work. Certification may be required on items that have been worked on, repaired or replaced, and this must be carried out before starting up. The biggest problem associated with hydrocarbons is fire and explosion, and any work that could provide a source of ignition must be eliminated or strictly controlled.

Water and Hydrates Presence and Removal

Water can cause a range of problems if introduced or allowed to accumulate in process plant. Water can flash to steam in processes operating above its boiling point, react violently with other chemicals, or cause long-term corrosion damage. Process removal of water and arrangements to prevent contamination by water are therefore important design and operational requirements.

Hydrates form when there is a drop in temperature of natural gas-containing water. These solid or semi-solid compounds, resembling ice crystals, can accumulate and impede the passage of natural gas through valves and gathering systems, causing blockages that could lead to ruptures. They can occur in a range of oil and gas activities such as drilling operations, offshore facilities, including sea-floor pipelines, and onshore plants such as refineries. Hydrates need to be removed from all hydrocarbon conveying systems, often requiring shutdown and venting in order to facilitate their removal.

Removal of sand, pyrophoric iron and low specific-activity (LSA) sludges often takes place with spades, blinds or spectacle blinds or slip plates. Entry into confined spaces requires a confined space-entry permit and all maintenance work, waste materials removal, etc. will be strictly controlled by the conditions set out in the permit.

Certain tests and inspections will be required before start-up

The controls required to minimise risks during plant shut-down and start-up include:

- Ensure work carried out under the controls of a permit-to-work.
- Services:
  - Stopped.
  - Isolated.
  - Drained down.
  - Blanked.
- Empty and drain hydrocarbon facilities, with all liquids, gases and residues removed leaving the plant safe to work on.
- Eliminate or strictly control any ignition sources.
- Strictly supervise and monitor activities throughout the duration of the work.
- Certification of items that have been worked on, repaired, or replaced before starting up.

- Establish:
  - All isolations re-made.
  - All blanks removed.
  - All tools and service equipment taken out of the area before commissioning and hook-up of the equipment. Ensure any required tests (pressures, temperatures, flow rates, etc.) are carried out.
- Ensure safety items (pressure-relief valves, diverter valves, bursting discs, etc.) are all functioning fully and correctly.
- Ensure pipework and system components are pressurised, pressure-tested and leak-tested (where repairs, modifications or alterations have taken place) before being functionally and operationally tested.
- Ensure integrity testing (non-destructive testing (NDT)) is carried out, where required, to check the quality of welds.
- Complete permit to ensure that all systems are put back into operable condition before start-up.
- Include in the permit (where necessary) an emergency plan, where emergency recovery and rescue are available, with full first-aid and fire-fighting facilities on hand during start-up.

Testing, Commissioning and Hook-Up

Following maintenance and before commissioning and hook-up of the equipment, it must be established that all isolations have been re-made, all blanks removed, and all tools and service equipment taken out of the area. This will be done as part of the final checks required on the permit-to-work.

There may be a requirement to carry out certain tests (pressures, temperatures, flow rates, etc.) and ensure safety items such as pressure relief valves, diverter valves, bursting discs, etc. are fully and correctly functioning. This is even more important where new components have been installed during the maintenance, and their correct and safe operation needs to be tested and assured.

Depending on the length of the shutdown, valves and drains may need to be checked to ensure they are in line before starting, and have not seized up during the inactive period.

Where repairs, modifications or alterations have taken place, pipework and some system components will need to be pressurised, pressure-tested and leak-tested, before being functionally and operationally tested. Integrity testing (non-destructive testing (NDT)) may be required to check the quality of welds.

When a specialist contractor has been involved, e.g. to install a new pump, testing and commissioning of plant before handover will be controlled by the permit-to-work system. Under such start-up conditions, the permit-to-work should include an emergency plan, similar to that required for work in confined spaces, where emergency recovery and rescue are available, with full first-aid and fire-fighting facilities on hand.

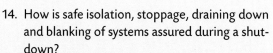

REVISION QUESTION

14. How is safe isolation, stoppage, draining down and blanking of systems assured during a shut-down?

(Suggested Answers are at the end.)

SUMMARY

This element has provided you with an introduction to hydrocarbon process safety. In particular, it has:

- Explained the principles of assessing and managing contractors, including the roles of parties involved.
- Discussed the management tools and the controls applicable to process safety management in the oil and gas industries.
- Given an explanation of the role and purpose of a permit-to-work system, with examples of appropriate permits.
- Discussed the key principles of a safe shift handover.
- Highlighted the importance of safe plant operation and maintenance of hydrocarbon-containing equipment and processes.
- Provided an outline of the hazards, risks and controls associated with safe shut-down and start-up of hydrocarbon containing equipment and processes.

Exam Skills

QUESTION

Identify the factors to be considered when assessing the health and safety competence of a contractor.　　(8)

APPROACHING THE QUESTION

- Using the system we have covered, the first thing to do is read the question carefully. You are asked to identify the factors, without being told how many are required. You should structure your approach (a list that can be developed to identify the main areas).
- Next, consider the marks available. For this question there are eight marks; we can presume that the question requires eight different considerations to be identified, so we could expect one mark for each. The question should take around eight minutes.
- Now highlight the key words. In this case, it might look like this:

  Identify the factors to be considered when assessing the health and safety competence of a contractor.

- Read the question again – make sure you understand it.
- Following this, the next stage is to develop a plan. A plan can be completed in various ways, but it could consist of the following:

SUGGESTED ANSWER

Plan

Consideration given for	
Experience	Qualifications and skills
Policy	Professional bodies
Risk assessments	Insurance
Accident record	References
Enforcement actions	Sub-contractor selection?
Method statements	Client liaison
Monitoring/inspections	

Now have a go at the question yourself.

Exam Skills

REASONS FOR POOR MARKS ACHIEVED BY CANDIDATES IN EXAM

- Not answering the question at all. If you do not attempt all questions required you cannot get any marks.
- Not following a structured approach: remember, the question didn't say how many considerations were required, but there were eight marks, so a minimum of eight should be attempted (it is probably safer to aim for 10, if you can).
- The question asked you to identify, so a list would not gain maximum marks.
- Giving lots of other information not relevant to the question, or applicable to considering contractors' health and safety.

HYDROCARBON PROCESS SAFETY 2

ELEMENT
3

LEARNING OUTCOMES

On completion of this element, you should be able to demonstrate understanding of the content by applying what you have learnt to familiar and unfamiliar situations. In particular, you should be able to:

1 Outline types of failure modes that may lead to loss of containment from hydrocarbons.

2 Outline types of failures that may lead to loss of containment from hydrocarbons.

3 Outline the controls available to maintain safety-critical equipment.

4 Outline the hazards, risks and controls available for safe containment of hydrocarbons offshore and onshore.

5 Outline the fire hazards, risks and controls relating to hydrocarbons.

6 Outline the hazards, risks and controls available for operating boilers and furnaces.

Contents

Failure Modes

FORCES ON MATERIALS

Any force imposed on an item made from any material is resisted by the internal structure of that material, and this internal force is equal and opposite to the force applied.

- Pulling (stretching) a material is known as a **tensile force**.
- Pushing a material is known as a **compressive force**.
- A force not applied in line is called a **shear force**.
- External forces can be **bending forces**.
- Twisting forces are known as **axial** or **torsional forces**.

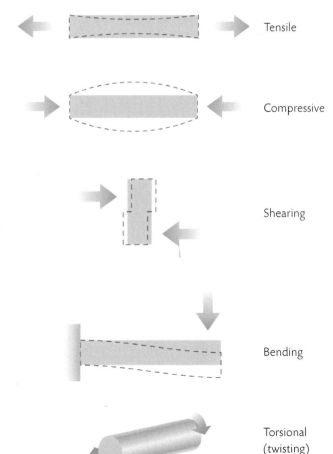

Tensile

Compressive

Shearing

Bending

Torsional
(twisting)

CREEP

At elevated temperature and with a constant load/stress applied close to the elastic limit, material may continue to deform slowly over time. This is essentially a slow process of plastic deformation referred to as **creep**.

The extent to which creep acts depends on two main factors:

- Time.
- Temperature.

Creep is a major factor in hot, high-pressure environments such as furnaces and turbines.

It is not a true mode of failure, as the failure will occur as either brittle or ductile, depending on the type of, and properties of, the parent material. However, it is a specific factor that has to be considered, particularly as it is time-dependent.

Creep has been known to lead to:

- Excessive deformation in turbine blades.
- Rupture of pressure systems, e.g. fractured steam pipes.

Creep is primarily controlled by design, in the shape of the components and the choice of materials, e.g. chrome-molybdenum steels have low creep characteristics.

Failure Modes

STRESS

When material is heated it expands. If this expansion cannot occur because the material is constrained, it will impose a **stress** on the material.

> ### GLOSSARY
>
> **STRESS**
> The force applied per unit area.
>
> **STRAIN**
> The fractional distortion due to the stress (e.g. the amount a material stretches compared to its original size).

The term **strain** is used to compare the ability of a material to change length when subject to compressive or tensile forces.

Strain is a ratio of the extension over the original length:

Strain = Change in length / Original length

When a material is distorted by forces acting on it, it is said to be in a state of strain, where strain is the ratio:

Deflection / Dimension of material

Effects of Loading

If loads are not too excessive, materials will return to their original size when the load is removed, in an **elastic** manner. With higher stresses the deformation becomes permanent, the material does not return to its original size, and the material is plastically deformed. **Tensile strength** is the maximum force necessary to cause a fracture.

If a material is stressed beyond its **yield point** varying degrees of permanent extension or distortion will occur. The tensile strength of a material is therefore a useful guide to its mechanical properties, as is the yield point.

During operation, either the body of a vessel or pipework system, or parts in the assembly, may be subjected to stresses.

Stress can arise from:

- Periodic fluctuations in operating pressure.
- Temperature cycling.
- Vibration.
- Water hammer.
- Periodic fluctuations of external loads.

Fatigue failure will occur during the service life of the vessel if the endurance limit is exceeded.

Principal Stresses

Failure of a simple structural element under tensile or compressive stress relates to the tensile strength of the material but components may be subjected to combined stresses.

For example, thermal stress can be caused by differential expansion of a vessel due to different temperatures or the use of different materials. Other sources of secondary stresses are the constraints arising at flanges or supports, and changes of section due to reinforcement at openings or connections.

Although such stresses do not affect the bursting strength of a vessel, they are important considerations when the vessel is subject to repeated pressure loading. If local yielding has occurred, residual stress when the pressure load is removed, and repeated pressure cycling can lead to fatigue failure.

For design purposes it is necessary to decide a value for the maximum allowable stress that can be accepted by a material. This can be done by applying a factor of safety to the maximum stress that the material could be expected to withstand in standard test conditions. The factor allows for any discrepancies in design, the loading, the quality of the materials and the workmanship. Selection of suitable material must take into account the suitability for fabrication (particularly welding) as well as the environment.

Effect of Stress

Corrosion rate and the form of attack can be changed if a material is under stress. Generally, the rate of attack will not change significantly within normal design stress values, but for some combinations of metals, corrosion media and temperature, stress cracking can occur. This is the general name given to a form of attack in which cracks are produced and grow rapidly. This can cause premature brittle fracture of the metal.

STRESS-CORROSION CRACKING

Stress-corrosion cracking occurs when **three criteria appear together**:

- A susceptible material.
- A corrosive environment.
- Enough tensile stress to induce the condition.

Examples of stress-corrosion cracking include caustic embrittlement of steel boilers and the stress-corrosion cracking of stainless steels in the presence of chloride ions.

Stress corrosion is worse:

- In corrosive environments.
- At elevated temperatures.

It is more common in alloys than pure metals, and particularly where there is exposure to chemicals. This is seen when:

- Aluminium alloys crack from exposure to chloride.
- Mild steels crack from exposure to nitrates.
- Copper and its alloys crack from exposure to ammonia.

Stress-corrosion cracking can be avoided by selecting materials not susceptible in the specific corrosion environment or, less certainly, by annealing after fabrication welding.

Corrosion fatigue describes the premature failure of materials in corrosive environments caused by **cyclic stresses**. Even mildly corrosive conditions can markedly reduce the fatigue life of a component. Unlike stress-corrosion cracking, corrosion fatigue can occur in any corrosive environment and does not depend on a specific combination of corrosive substance and metal. For safety-critical components subjected to cyclic stresses, material with a high resistance to corrosion must be specified.

THERMAL SHOCK

GLOSSARY

THERMAL SHOCK
The effect of cracking that results from rapid and extreme temperature changes, e.g. from hot to cold and vice versa.

Thermal shock makes material expand and contract, so setting up cyclic stress reversal and leading to fatigue failure. Different parts of an object expand by different amounts, causing expansion to occur unevenly. It can be regarded in terms of stress and strain. At some point the stress will overcome the strength of the material, causing it to crack. If preventive measures are not used, the crack will continue until the object/material fails. Thermal shock can be prevented by ensuring temperature changes occur more slowly, or increasing the strength of the material.

An example of thermal shock might be a brittle fracture from stress or strain across a weld in ductile material.

BRITTLE FRACTURE

Brittle fractures occur suddenly and without warning, when an excessive load is placed on a structure and the material is not able to slip, either owing to the structure of the material itself or because insufficient time is available owing to the intensity of the load. Small cracks spread through the material so quickly that a massive failure is produced. Failure can occur with the applied stresses below the yield stress.

The speed of failure often results in some of the energy in the material at failure being released as sound, giving the brittle fracture a characteristic "crack", or loud bang. Brittle fracture can also be part of the sequence in other failure modes (e.g. ductile).

TOPIC FOCUS

Factors that promote brittle fracture include:

- Low temperature – the temperature can affect failure in a brittle or ductile mode. The effect is particularly important for materials that are subject to cold weather, and for LPG cylinders and systems.
- Impact or "snatch" loading – can produce very high levels of stress very quickly, particularly in such items as lifting equipment. When subject to such loading, the material does not have time to spread the load evenly throughout the crystalline boundaries, thus producing high areas of stress. When failure occurs in these areas it then propagates throughout the material and total failure occurs.
- Residual tensile stresses – stresses "built into" the structure of the material during fabrication or assembly, e.g. beams being pulled together, or in the vicinity of welds. These tensile stresses act within the loading, leading to brittle fracture, effectively "pre-loading" the material.
- Inherently brittle material – some materials have an atomic structure that has difficulty giving way under stress and will fail by brittle fracture. Such materials include cast iron, glass and ceramics.

Brittle fractures:

- Will not show signs of deformation.
- The cross-sectional area at the break will look like the original component.
- The surface will be "bright" – showing no signs of corrosion, and occasionally having "chevron" (v-shaped) markings across the fractured surface.

Failure Modes

Brittle fracture of welded structures is dependent on:

- Plate thickness.
- Residual stresses present after fabrication.
- The operating temperature.

MEANING OF "SAFE OPERATING ENVELOPE"

The process designer is trying to achieve a controlled chemical reaction process that prevents a hazardous situation from occurring. The **safe operating envelope** defines the boundaries that contain the controlled reaction. In this safe operating envelope, safety is determined within the designer's boundaries (often with upper and lower limits). Safe operation requires definition of how violations beyond the limits and system failures are to be detected and corrected. There may be design constraints that allow fault tolerance and recovery, providing there are adequate warning systems to indicate system over-run or failure.

Modern process facilities rely heavily on fault detection, alarm systems and safety-instrumented systems to maintain operations within this clearly defined safe operating envelope. If respected, the safe operating limits set at the process and mechanical design stage ensure safe operation of the equipment and process.

Operating plant changes with age and inevitably undergoes maintenance, modifications and alterations over time. The limits may physically alter but are critical at all times for safe operation.

Typical issues at a process well, for example, may include changes in flow parameters, changes in gas or effluent composition, annular pressures, corrosion or wear. Changes in these parameters should be monitored and recorded so that maintenance systems can be adjusted to deal with abnormalities.

USE OF KNOWLEDGE OF FAILURE MODES IN INITIAL DESIGN, PROCESS AND SAFE OPERATION

When the design loads of a vessel, pipework, or equipment have been determined and the maximum stresses due to the design loads have been calculated, the designer must qualitatively evaluate the individual stresses by type (since not all stresses or their combinations require the same safety factors in protection against failure).

When a pressure part is loaded to beyond the yield point by a mechanical (static) force, such as internal pressure in a pipe or weight on a vessel, the yielding can continue until the part breaks.

While design criteria provide the necessary formulas to calculate the required thickness and the stresses of the basic vessel components due to internal load and external pressures, it leaves it up to the designer to calculate the stresses due to other loads.

Creep can cause excessive deformation in turbine blades and the rupture of pressure systems, and its prevention should be controlled by careful design of the shape of the components and the choice of materials, e.g. chrome-molybdenum steels have low creep characteristics.

Designers should also consider material that will avoid thermal shock, in that their strength is sufficient to withstand it, or that the material has appropriate thermal conductivity and heat capacity for the conditions in which it will operate.

FAILURE OF THE ANNULAR RIM

> ### GLOSSARY
>
> **ANNULAR RIM**
> The name given to the bottom rim of a storage tank.

The rim and bottom plates of storage tanks will corrode rapidly if the fluids stored in them have high sea-water content, e.g. crude oil tanks. The sea water will corrode the base plates and rim faster than other parts of the structure, and pitting corrosion will be a significant feature.

Another issue is settlement of the tank into or onto a foundation, and even settlement of the foundation itself. The settlement will also lead to corrosion as the joints and protective finishes are affected by the movement.

Tanks for hydrocarbon products (crude oils, etc.) that have high sulphur content also exhibit bacterial corrosion with deeper pitting corrosion penetrating bottom plates and the rim, causing leaks.

The result of this corrosion and settlement will be mechanical failure of the rim and bottom plates, leading to loss of containment.

> ### REVISION QUESTIONS
>
> 1. Describe three forces that may be imposed on a surface or object.
> 2. Explain the term "creep".
> 3. What are the conditions necessary for stress corrosion cracking to occur?
> 4. Describe TWO of the factors that promote brittle fracture.
>
> (Suggested Answers are at the end.)

Other Types of Failures

WELD FAILURES

Welding is a commonly used method of fabrication of pressure vessel shells, pipework systems and installation structures. Structural, non-pressure parts are also often attached to a vessel wall by welding, e.g. stiffening rings, lifting lugs, support clips for piping, internal trays and other equipment. Welded joints, instead of bolted joints, are sometimes used for piping-to-vessel connections to obtain optimum leakproof design. The most widely used industrial welding method is arc welding.

Residual stresses in a weld and in the region adjacent to a weld are unavoidable and complex, but they are not considered dangerous when a static load is applied. If the weld residual stress is added to the stress caused by an external load and exceeds the yield point of the material, a small amount of plastic yielding will redistribute the stress. This is particularly true for ductile materials, and one important requirement for a good weld is high ductility.

To prevent loss of ductility in heat-affected zones, only low-carbon, non-hardenable steels are used as construction material. In addition, the residual stresses in heavier plates are usually removed by post-weld heat treatment. Cooling after welding causes dimensional changes in the weld due to temperature reduction and phase change; these changes may result in occasional cracking in the weld, or the heat-affected zones around the weld.

The strength of a welded joint will depend on the type of joint and the quality of the welding. The soundness of welds is checked by visual inspection and non-destructive testing.

Visual Inspection

This involves looking at the welding using either the naked eye, a magnifying glass, or (where it can be applied) a microscope, depending on the size of the object and the size of defect that it is being inspected for. This method will require a good light source, and the surface will require cleaning to remove any protective covering (e.g. paint). The inspector will need to have access to the surface. This is a relatively easy technique to use but it is limited to surface defect detection only. It can be applied to virtually all materials but may be time-consuming, as the whole weld surface must be effectively covered.

Non-Destructive Testing

Principles

The aim of non-destructive testing (NDT) is to test without having to destroy the integrity of the material, or the component.

Techniques

DYE PENETRANT

Involves the use of dye penetrant to highlight the defect so that the visual inspection described above can occur. Dye is applied by spraying and this penetrates into any surface crack. Dye absorbed into the defect indicates location.

MAGNETIC PARTICLE

Involves magnetising the component and applying magnetic particles or ink. Any defect in the component will show, as it distorts the magnetic field and the particles lie 'differently'.

EDDY CURRENT

High frequency AC current passed through a coil sets up alternating magnetic fields. The coil is placed next to the surface of an electrically conducting material and sets up eddy currents in the material. Any discontinuity in the surface causes a variation of the eddy current.

A second coil placed adjacent to the first can detect the changes in the eddy current, so indicating the location of a defect. These changes can be calibrated and used to determine the depth of any defect.

ULTRASONIC

Involves the use of a generator transmitting ultrasound waves into a material and detecting them when reflected from within the material. Any defect will cause a variation in the return signal and this can be interpreted to indicate the depth of the defect. It can detect defects within the material that do not show on the surface.

RADIOGRAPHY

Involves gamma or X-rays, which are passed through the material and onto a strip of film. The radiation darkens the film emulsion, which, when developed (radiographs), shows where any discontinuity/defect exists within the material. This is an important method where a permanent record of the inspection is required, and is used extensively in steel fabrication, particularly in highly-specified situations such as welds on oil rigs, pipework and reactor vessels.

Other Types of Failures

PRESSURE TESTING

Involves subjecting a finished pressure system to a test with the pressure at some value above the working pressure (normally 1.5 times working pressure). Liquid is often used because, in the event of failure, the pressure is released with the loss of relatively small amounts of liquid.

The following table summarises non-destructive testing methods:

Test	Advantages	Disadvantages
Visual	Quick and inexpensive.	Surface defects only. Surface must be clean and accessible.
Dye penetrant	Inexpensive and convenient. Superior to visual examination alone. For all non-porous materials.	Surface defects only. Defects must be open to the surface.
Magnetic particle	More sensitive than dye penetrant. Can also find sub-surface defects.	Ferrous metals only. Cannot find defects at any significant depth. Requires a power source.
Eddy current	Rapid detection of surface or sub-surface flaws. Can measure depth of shallow flaws.	Cannot operate close to other free surfaces, e.g. thin sheet. Cannot find deep flaws. Requires a power source.
Ultrasonic	Precise location of internal and external defects. Sizing of many defects possible.	Expensive equipment. Dependent on a skilled operator and a power supply.
Radiography	Permanent, pictorial, easily interpreted images obtained. Locates majority of internal defects.	Safety hazards (radiation). Expensive X-ray sets. Thickness limits (more so with X-rays). Power supply needed. Needs access to both sides.
Pressure testing	System can be tested while in operation.	Cleaning problem if hydraulic medium used in a gaseous system.

ADVANTAGES AND DISADVANTAGES OF NON-DESTRUCTIVE TESTING

Non-destructive testing is used extensively as one method of ensuring quality control, and as a tool for maintenance regimes to identify possible causes of failure. The range of techniques allows at least one method to be available in almost every situation. A key factor in this is the portability of test equipment.

To get the most out of non-destructive testing it is important to select the most appropriate technique for each particular situation. A particular option may, theoretically, seem to be the best choice but in practice there may be factors affecting its use, such as heat, cold, lack of access, etc., so another option should be considered.

Selecting the wrong technique may mean the wrong results are obtained, e.g. using magnetic particle detection on dirty surfaces will not positively identify faults.

This leads to the question of the acceptance of the results. The requirement for humans to interpret the results can lead to human error. The most significant aspect of non-destructive testing in recent years is the use of computers to record and interpret results.

> ## REVISION QUESTION
>
> 5. Outline the advantages and disadvantages of the different non-destructive testing techniques.
>
> (Suggested Answers are at the end.)

Safety-Critical Equipment Controls

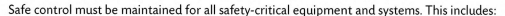

KEY INFORMATION

Safe control must be maintained for all safety-critical equipment and systems. This includes:

- Emergency shut-down (ESD) equipment and systems.
- Safety integrity levels (SIL) for instrumentation.
- Procedures for bypassing ESD, but which are not to be bypassed without considering the consequences – testing and logging.
- Blow-down facilities and flare types.
- Closed and open drain headers, sewers, and interceptors.

SAFETY CONTROL

Safety-critical equipment includes:

- Process equipment controls.
- Fire and gas controls.
- Emergency shut-down.
- Drilling systems.

Process Equipment

Process equipment controls should be monitored throughout operating cycles, and mechanical and electronic/instrumentation systems should be in place to identify and shut down in case of faults or malfunctions in the systems, particularly where high-integrity functions are involved. These include SCADA (supervisory control and data acquisition) systems (see later), programmable logic controllers (PLCs) and PLC programmers, distributed and batch-control systems. These are called emergency shut-down systems. They include such protection as pressure and temperature relief and flow parameter controls (flow rates/volumes in pipework, etc). Collectively, these are known as HIPS (High-Integrity Protection Systems).

Where there is no independent mechanical protection system in place instrumentation will be provided, but it must be of high integrity, having high failure-to-safety built in, as well as being highly fault-tolerant with redundancy systems. Systems must be fast to respond to detected malfunctions outside normal safe operating envelopes. In their *Loss of Containment Manual*, the UK HSE advises, for instance, that for ESD systems, in order to achieve required response times, pressure transmitters are preferred to pressure switches in HIPS.

Fire and Gas Controls

Paramount to fire safety are the segregation of hazardous and non-hazardous areas of the installation, and adequate access, escape routes and safe havens for personnel. To support this, fire and gas detection and protection systems will be in place.

Fire and gas controls (including their ESD) are designed to protect the installation, plant and personnel from hazardous fires and emergencies involving gas. They monitor the areas on the installation where fire can occur and a build-up of flammable atmospheres is likely. The fire and gas systems can detect hazardous events, and built-in alarm systems will alert control personnel and set off the ESD so that the consequences of these events are minimised. They operate through a number of fire and gas detectors (detecting flame, smoke, temperature, rate of temperature rise, etc. at the critical locations) and feed all this data through the integral ESD system so that the automatic shut-down is started if a hazardous event occurs.

EMERGENCY SHUT-DOWN EQUIPMENT AND SYSTEMS

ESD systems are intended to monitor and detect faults in processes and service systems. When detected, they will shut down to prevent escalation of a hazardous event and protect people and property on the installation from damage.

An example of this is the protection system for gas compressors shown in the following figure. Compressors are used to pressurise hydrocarbon gas and a surge vessel prevents major fluctuations in flow to the compressor. During normal conditions, gas flows into the surge vessel and onto the motor-driven compressor. However, it is possible for liquids to accumulate in the surge vessel and then enter the compressor. Consequently, during abnormal conditions an undesirable liquid level can form in the surge vessel, which could lead to catastrophic compressor damage. To protect against this the surge vessel is fitted with instrumentation to detect liquids. The Distributed Control System (DCS) controls the process generally and under abnormal conditions, providing information to the control room operating panel, but for extreme emergency conditions hardwired independent detection and controls systems are used.

Safety-Critical Equipment Controls

In the illustrated system there are three levels of instrument protection:

- At 10% vessel capacity a high-level alarm operates in the control room through the DCS.
- At 50% vessel capacity the detection system communicates with the DCS and initiates an emergency shutdown.
- At 60% vessel capacity a detection system that operates independently of the DCS directly initiates an emergency shutdown.

The system is designed to alert the operators to abnormal conditions, take emergency action if the alert is not responded to, and initiate an independent emergency shutdown if action is not taken through the DCS.

All ESD systems should be separate and independent to normal production controls, so that common-cause failures can be avoided. Control valves should be independent within ESD systems, and not used for dual control or shut-down, as they are not designed for tight shut-off.

All shut-down and blowdown valves should fail-to-safety, and those for isolating pipework and systems should always fail closed. Blowdown valves, on the other hand, should fail open if power supply or control signals are lost due to system failure. Justification will be needed (in safety cases) where fail-safe is not integral to the ESD system.

Where bypass systems are provided around shutdown valves for maintenance purposes, they should be locked closed with the shut-down valve handwheels removed. Valves on hydraulic-system return lines themselves can cause failure, so should be locked open.

Drilling Systems

These should be monitored for all operational functions and services. Mechanical systems should be in place (e.g. on well-deck and drilling units) to control the drilling process, and systems should monitor and control water, steam and sludges for pressurisation and lubrication. These will also monitor the collection and transport of oil and gas through the systems to the surface. Again, system monitors should be in place connected through ESD systems in the event of critical controls malfunctioning.

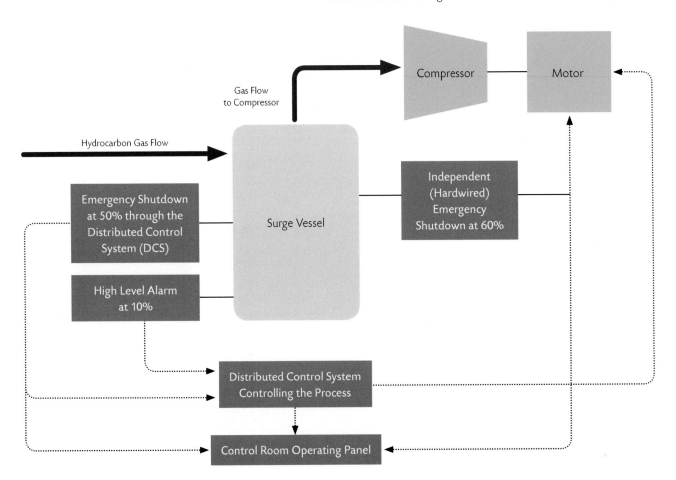

Instrument Protection for Compressor

SAFETY INTEGRITY LEVELS FOR INSTRUMENTATION

Every instrumented protective function should have its safety criticality established, usually indicated by using safety integrity levels (SILs). There are generally four levels, each corresponding to a range of "likelihood of failure" targets. SIL 1 will be at the highest Probability of Failure on Demand (PFD) and SIL 4 the lowest PFD. The higher the safety integrity level, the more critical the safety function, e.g. trip systems, fire and gas, HIPS, relief and blowdown systems.

Operational documentation should indicate which instrumented functions have been designated safety-critical elements and what their criticality rating (SIL) is. Their trip settings should be indicated in a 'trip register', together with procedures for proof testing and the intervals between testing.

All safety-critical instrumented protective functions need regular tests to prove that their performance standards continue to be met, and all test results should be recorded. The higher the integrity of the system, the more stringent testing will be required. Often, testing is broken down into different processes looking at sensors, logic and final end elements of the process. Sensors can have their logic inhibited to make more regular testing possible (anything from monthly to annually), but the logic and process end elements cannot be easily over-ridden, so an actual trip of operating plant is required, making such testing less frequent.

It is important that all production control functions are separate from protective functions so that common failures can be avoided.

PROCEDURES FOR BYPASSING ESD

Emergency shut-down systems should not generally have by-pass (inhibiting or override) facilities unless they are very closely controlled, and only operated under permit conditions. As we saw earlier, where bypass systems are provided around shutdown valves for maintenance purposes, they should be locked closed under normal operating conditions with the shutdown valve handwheels removed. Remember that valves on hydraulic system return lines themselves can cause failure, so should be locked open under normal operating conditions.

All bypass of ESD system proposals should be generated and authorised by a competent person, and suitable justification should be given. Adequate risk assessment should be carried out of the proposed bypass, which should reveal the safe conditions and controls required.

Bypasses of ESD systems should be applied for the shortest possible periods of time, and any continued application must be monitored and controlled, particularly at critical times, such as shift hand-over.

All ESD bypass systems should be tested to ensure they function correctly, and full testing of the ESD system should be carried out after reversal to ensure ESDs function correctly when reinstated. All operation of such bypasses should be entered in a bypass log, recording the conditions of the bypass (e.g. the equipment involved, systems affected), the time and date and any cross-reference to permit-to-work forms that apply. Similar entries of time and date are required for each assessment of the ESD bypass, and when the bypass is removed.

The number of bypasses should be controlled so that the number in place does not become detrimental to safe operations and remains easy to manage at all times.

Safety-Critical Equipment Controls

BLOWDOWN FACILITIES AND FLARE TYPES

Blowdown

> **GLOSSARY**
>
> **BLOWDOWN**
> The term commonly used to describe the removal of liquid content from process vessels and equipment to reduce the likelihood of fires or explosions occurring.

Blowdown is similar to depressurisation carried out in gas process systems.

Blowdown from liquid process systems should not be sent through a flare that is only designed and intended to handle gases, as liquids passed through these flares may result in flame-outs. If the flare is elevated, such liquid discharges may then be spread over the facility, or other outlying areas. The best practice is to route liquid blowdown to facilities that are designed to handle large quantities of liquid materials – perhaps a storage tank, open pit or another process area, or a pressurised sewer intended for this purpose.

Blowdown to tanks is generally avoided because any gases from the liquids can be released and become entrapped in the tank, causing it to rupture. Open pits are not really practical, as they will allow open release of combustible liquids and their vapours.

Liquid carry-over has been noted during blowdowns offshore.

Flaring

Gas flares are widely used in the oil and gas industries, as well as chemical and petrochemical plants. They are also used with well-drilling operations, at oil rigs and gasoline refineries.

A gas flare, or flare-stack, is a tall discharge facility used to eliminate waste gas that is not required in other processes or for transportation. Flares can also act as safety systems for non-waste gases, venting process gases through pressure relief systems. In emergency situations, the flare can burn out total reserve gas.

There are fixed and portable flare stacks, which can be self-supporting structures, or stacks supported by guys, derricks, or can be tripod type.

On oil and gas production installations, the flare acts as a safety device that will protect vessels and pipework from becoming over-pressurised from non-routine incidents and process faults.

If plant and equipment become over-pressurised, pressure-relief valves in the system will operate to automatically release pressure, in some cases relieving both gas and liquids. These will be routed through a 'knock-out' drum and through large flare-header pipework systems to the flare stack. The gases (and liquids) will be burned off as they are emitted through the flare stack.

In the case of dirty flares such as this, steam is often injected into the flame at the tip of the stack to reduce the black smoke, but this does tend to make the flare much noisier. In more advanced flare-tip designs, wet steam at the tip can be prevented from freezing (leading to flame-out) by injecting gas continually at the tip, acting as a 'pilot-light', so that the flare remains ready at all times and the system is always ready to perform its primary purpose as an over-pressure safety system. A further advantage of the flare-tip 'pilot-light' is that it aids complete combustion when dilute gases are burned. Enclosed ground flares can be used, which are designed and constructed to eliminate smoke and keep the flame within the stack.

Flares can produce a range of undesirable effects and by-products, such as noise, smoke, heat, light, radiation, and various combustion and thermal decomposition products as gases. Most of these can be minimised by good design and engineering systems.

Flare Types

There are two categories of flare – those determined by the **height of the flare-tip**, and those described by the **mixing method** used at the flare-tip. In virtually all flare types, the combustion of the materials occurs through a diffusion flame where air is used to diffuse across the boundary of the fuel stream in towards the centre of the fuel flow, forming an envelope containing a combustible mixture of gases around the core of fuel gas. This creates a stable flame at the flare-tip. A good supply of air must be maintained and air/gas mixing kept efficient to ensure complete combustion and reduction of smoke.

The type of flare will depend on such factors as the available space at the installation, and the characteristics of the flare gas (its composition, pressure, quantity, etc). Its main features must always be safety and reliability while continuing to prevent the release of unburned gases.

STEAM-ASSISTED FLARES

Steam-assisted flares have single burner tips and are elevated above ground to burn vented gas in a diffusion flame. Most refineries and chemical plants use this type of flare. Steam is injected into the combustion zone to promote turbulence for mixing and to induce air into the flame. This ensures an adequate air supply and good mixing.

AIR-ASSISTED FLARES

Air-assisted flares use forced air for combustion and mixing and give a relatively smoke-free flame. The burner has many small gas orifices in a spider-shaped pattern inside at the top of a steel cylinder, and the air for combustion is provided by a fan in the bottom of the cylinder. The fan speed can alter the amount of air for combustion. These are handy for use where there is no steam available. They are not usually used with large flares.

NON-ASSISTED FLARES

Simple flare tips without any steam or air-mixing facility, and limited to gas streams with a low heat content and a low ratio of hydrogen/carbon that will burn well without producing lots of smoke. They manage with less air to give complete combustion and have lower combustion temperatures.

PRESSURE-ASSISTED FLARES

Pressure-assisted flares use the vent-stream pressure to assist with mixing the combustible fuels at the burner tip. Where there is enough vent-stream pressure they can be used on flare tips that would have used steam or air to give a smokeless discharge. They have a number of burner heads, which operate depending on the amount of gas to be discharged. Although not exclusively, this type normally has its burner arrangement at ground level, so has to be located in a remote plant area with adequate space.

ENCLOSED GROUND FLARES

Enclosed ground flares have burner heads enclosed in an internally insulated shell, which helps cut down smoke, noise, luminosity and heat radiation and protects from the wind. Adequate mixing is achieved by a high nozzle pressure-drop, so air or steam assistance is not needed. The height of the flare tip must be adequate to create a draught to supply enough air to give smokeless combustion and to allow the thermal plume to disperse. These flares will always be located at ground level. They have less capacity than an open flare and work well with continuous, constant-flow vent streams.

Flare Monitoring

Flare monitoring should be in place to ensure the integrity of the emission and the flame. This will entail the use of various monitoring equipment, such as thermocouple sensors (usually placed within the flame for continuous monitoring), UV flame sensors, remote flame sensors and flue analysers, which monitor the condition of the mix of fluids and gases in the stack.

DRAINS, SEWERS AND INTERCEPTORS

On offshore installations drains usually consist of a series of **non-hazardous open drains** and **hazardous closed drainage systems**. The open drains are open to the atmosphere and closed drains are connected directly to pressure vessels.

OPEN DRAINS

Open-drain waters can include drainage from normal ground waters (rainwater and wash down from hoses, etc.), and from areas with hazardous safety ratings (water that may contain oil, etc.), and are routed to open-drain caissons and passed through interceptors and/or skimmers to clear away any oil and residues before the waters are discharged.

Open drains taking waste of a non-hazardous nature generally return it to an oil-drain tank and then to an injection unit to feed it into downhole re-injection.

Open-drain caissons are usually fitted with an extraction point, where samples can be taken and tested and which will be regularly monitored for cleanliness and oil content.

CLOSED DRAINS

Closed drains will be fed to high-pressure and low-pressure closed drainage drums. Once the liquids have been drained from the vessel, gas contained and released from the closed drain drums will be fed to a flare and liquids sent to a separator to be re-treated. Liquids in a closed-drain system can contain hydrocarbons that will "flash" in the drain system and can become a hazard, particularly if a closed-drain valve is inadvertently left open.

Closed-drain systems should never have any interconnection with an open-drain system, as gases will flashover into them. They may then travel and appear in 'safe' areas where there may be ignition sources, such as hot process exhausts and boilers.

Safety Critical Equipment Controls

SEWAGE

Sewage can be collected through a sewer system and put through a treatment plant, which often involves maceration and chlorination of the waste. Treated sewage can then be mixed with sea water and untreated 'domestic' water (from washrooms, laundry, etc), which is then discharged through a sewage caisson. Organic food wastes from galleys is also macerated and discharged through a sewage caisson. Since 1990, offshore installations can dispose of sewage directly into the sea.

PROCESS DRAIN WATER

Process drain water is a by-product where crude oil is pumped or where drilling takes place. This water is polluted with oil and cannot be discharged into the sea until it has gone through a cleansing and de-oiling process. Drain water is therefore passed through a separator unit, which commonly heats the contaminated water and inserts appropriate treatment additives, before separating it into liquids, oils and solid fractions (sludge). Separated oils will be sent to and stored in a waste oil tank, solids will be dried and disposed of and the water will be discharged into the sea when the oil content is low enough (the International Maritime Organisation (IMO) generally set the oil content limit at 15ppm).

INTERCEPTORS

Interceptors are used at onshore installations, mainly to collect and separate ground waters that fall and are drained from hazardous areas, or process waters that are discharged. These consist of a series of settling bays, which allow water to flow through the series of bays, while oil stays on the top and is collected in one area. This is then sucked out and disposed of.

Offshore, interceptors are often referred to as oil/water separators, which separate oil from water before it is discharged into the sea. There are legal limits to which oil containment in water can be disposed of overboard, and an official log has to be kept of sampling (usually done every 12 hours). More modern rigs will use carousel sampling apparatus.

If too much oil accumulates in the separator oil will escape. Full retention separators should be provided with an automatic closure device and a high-level alarm to indicate that immediate maintenance is required. They should also be provided with a visual and audible warning that the level of oil is high and immediate emptying of the separator is required for it to continue to work effectively.

> ## MORE...
>
> You can refer to the UK HSE *Loss of Containment Manual* (2007) by accessing:
>
> www.hse.gov.uk
>
> You can find more information on oil/water separators in the Environment Agency pollution prevention guideline publication *Use and design of oil separators in surface water drainage systems*: PPG 3 (April 2006) at:
>
> http://publications.environment-agency.gov.uk/PDF/PMHO0406BIYL-E-E.pdf with useful illustrations available in the ITALTRACO publication at:
>
> www.etna-usa.com/zertech.pdf
>
> and the US Environmental Protection Agency guidance at:
>
> www.epa.gov/oem/docs/oil/spcc/guidance/5_OWSeparators.pdf

> ## REVISION QUESTIONS
>
> 6. Why should all ESD systems be separate and independent of normal production controls?
> 7. What precautions are required when maintenance by-pass valves are installed around shut-down valves?
> 8. What does the term 'blowdown' refer to?
> 9. What are the purposes of a gas flare or 'flare-stack'?
> 10. Identify three different flare types.
>
> (Suggested Answers are at the end.)

Safe Storage of Hydrocarbons

HAZARDS AND RISKS

Storage tanks have different types of fire hazards depending on the type of tank. The most common fire hazards in above-ground tanks are overfilling, vent fires and rim-seal fires on floating-roof tanks. These can also give rise to full-surface fires, which are further divided into obstructed full-surface fires and unobstructed full-surface fires. Each type of fire will have different prevention controls depending on the tank type and cause of fire.

Overfilling

Fuel storage tanks can be overfilled because of:

- Failure of the operator to monitor filling (when filling manually).
- Failure of the pumping system to shut-off.
- Lack of or failure of over-filling sensors and alarms.
- Blockage or lack of adequate tank venting or relief systems.

Buncefield, 11 December 2005

Just after 6am on 11 December 2005 a series of explosions and subsequent fires destroyed large parts of the oil storage and transfer depot at Buncefield, near Hemel Hempstead in Hertfordshire, UK. One huge explosion was followed by a large fire, which spread to 23 large fuel storage tanks. The incident injured 43 people, but luckily there were no fatalities.

The main cause is thought to be the **overfilling of a floating-roof gasoline tank** (tank 912). This tank was one of three storage tanks contained in a common bund, the capacity of which was thought to be sufficient (110% of the largest tank), but spillage into the bund from any one tank would affect all tanks in the bund in the case of a fire. This questions the value of common bunding rather than individual bunds for each tank.

During delivery of fuel into tank 912 the **level controls and alarms failed** and the tank was overfilled. Around 250,000 litres of gasoline came out through the roof vents and cascaded down the tank sides into the bund. The heavier-than-air gasoline vapours filled and overflowed the bund. There was little or no wind at the time of the overfill, and a vapour cloud of hydrocarbon vapours and air was formed, which spread over a wide area.

Effects of Pressure and Vacuum

In tanks that operate with an internal pressure, pressure and vacuum valves are used to prevent or minimise the problems that may arise. Over-pressurisation can cause stress on the joints and seals in tank panels, and those with floating roofs can have roofs lifted or torn if pressure is not relieved, leading to leaks. **Pressure valves** have a vent built in that will open when a pre-set pressure is reached, such as when fuel is being pumped into the tank.

To prevent distortion from vacuum effects (negative pressure) **vacuum valves** have a relief vent that operates when a set vacuum value is reached, such as when a tank is being pumped empty.

Emergency pressure valves will also be used to release any sudden rise in pressure beyond the settings of the normal vent relief valves, e.g. if external heat of fire occurs in close proximity to the tank.

Safe Storage of Hydrocarbons

Failure of Tank Shells

Tank shells can fail owing to natural forces and pressures exerted by the wind or earthquakes. Corrosion can reduce the thickness of tanks and affect the metal components and operational errors; poor installation and deformation of the structure can lead to failure, as can settlement of foundations and tank bases.

Many tank-shell failures occur because of faulty welding, or the use of sub-standard steels in manufacture. Other structural issues include shell thickness inadequate for the pressure or vacuum conditions, or insufficient thickness to withstand the (repeated) loading of the contents, or failure to/lack of hydraulic testing to prove the tank's strength.

Much higher risk failure occurs as a result of flammable and explosive atmospheres within tanks, usually when 'empty' and set off by heat or ignition sources, such as burning or welding. For example, over-pressurisation of tanks when refilling can cause expansion of the shell and weaken seals. The effects of vacuum when tanks are being emptied can also be a problem, generally causing inward movement and warping of the shell, again with damage to joints and seals.

Corrosion – especially at ground level on the annular rim and in damaged areas (knocks, dents and scratches in the surface coating) – causes the shell to weaken at the local points of damage.

We shall look at tank design and construction later.

FLOATING-ROOF TANKS

As the name suggests, the roofs on these tanks 'float' – they can move up and down within the outer shell of the tank, always remaining immediately above the surface of the liquid contained, minimising the air gap and potential build-up of flammable hydrocarbon vapours.

There are two main types of floating-roof tank: those with an external floating roof only, and those with an internal floating roof beneath a standard fixed roof.

The **external floating-roof tank** is commonly used to store medium flashpoint hydrocarbon products in large quantities – particularly naphtha, kerosene, diesel and crude oil. The tank has an open-topped cylindrical steel shell with a roof inside the shell, which floats on the surface of the liquid in the tank, and will rise and fall with the liquid as its level changes.

The tank has a rim seal in place between the main shell of the tank and the floating roof to cut down on vapour evaporation and escape through the floating roof. The roof will have support legs that hang down into the liquid. This means that when fuel is at low level the roof lands on the base of the tank and a vapour space will form between the liquid surface and the roof, as it would in a standard fixed-roof tank. The legs can be retractable to increase the usability of the tank volume.

This type of tank gives economic benefits of preventing or reducing fuel loss and cutting down the emission of volatile organic compounds (VOCs). Disadvantages can be problems caused by rain and snow, which may accumulate on the roof, possibly causing the roof to sink. Water from the roof of these tanks can be drained through flexible hoses from a sump on the roof, often passing through the stored liquid in the tank down to the base of the tank, where it can be discharged through control valves.

A major disadvantage with external floating-roof tanks is the danger from lightning, which can cause ignition at the rim around the roof seal, causing major tank fires.

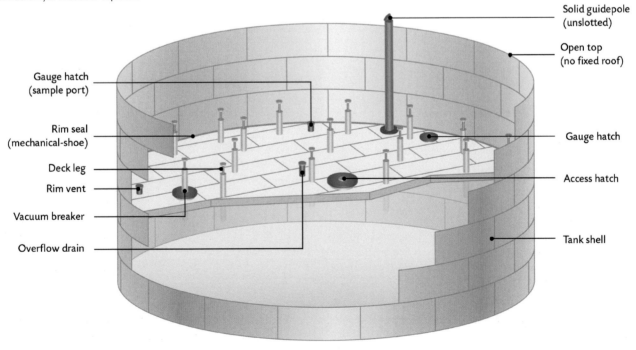

An External Floating-Roof Tank

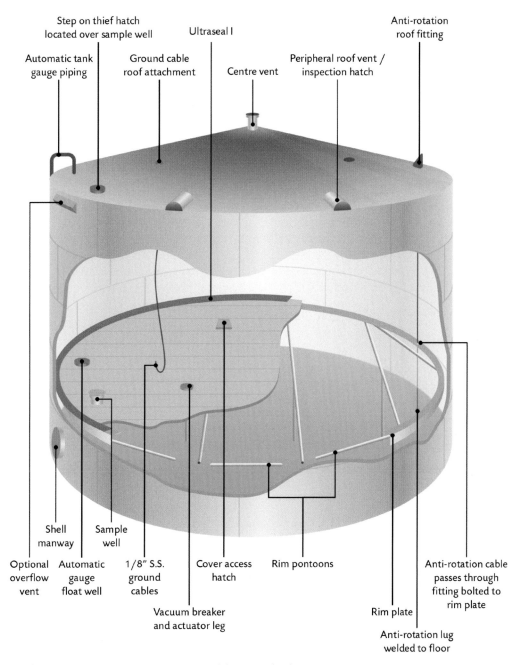

Automatic tank gauge piping

Step on thief hatch located over sample well

Ground cable roof attachment

Ultraseal I

Centre vent

Peripheral roof vent / inspection hatch

Anti-rotation roof fitting

Optional overflow vent

Shell manway

Automatic gauge float well

Sample well

1/8" S.S. ground cables

Vacuum breaker and actuator leg

Cover access hatch

Rim pontoons

Rim plate

Anti-rotation cable passes through fitting bolted to rim plate

Anti-rotation lug welded to floor

An Internal Floating-Roof Tank

Internal floating roofs will generally be used for storing the lower flashpoint hydrocarbons, such as gasoline, ethanol, etc. These tanks can overcome some of the weather-related problems of external floating-roof tanks.

In both types, as well as being able to 'land' or sink the roof to a low level, there is usually a facility to prevent the roof from rotating in the tank while floating.

These tanks have vents built into the fixed roof, and usually inspection hatches. Internal floating-roof tanks will reduce the likelihood of lightning strikes igniting vapours at the rim seal of the floating roof, cutting down the potential for tank fires.

FIXED-ROOF STORAGE TANKS

Design and Construction

Fixed-roof storage tanks are intended for use with liquids that have very high flash points (i.e. of low volatility, such as water, bitumen, etc.). Tanks should be constructed of steel, or other material suitable to withstand the effects of direct flames or radiant heat from a fire in the vicinity. They should be designed and constructed in accordance with the appropriate recognised standards and good engineering practice.

When the material to be used in the construction of the tank has been selected, consideration should be given to the chemical and physical properties of the contents to ensure they are compatible and will not cause, or lead to failure of the tank.

Safe Storage of Hydrocarbons

Tanks should be protected by a coating adequate to **resist corrosion**. For example, the external surface of tanks for onshore underground placement should be shot-blasted clean, or chemically primed and then coated with hot-applied bitumen reinforced with glass or synthetic fibre, or some equally resisting coating.

After tanks have been placed in position, the external surfaces should be inspected for damage.

After installation, but before being filled, a tank should undergo hydraulic leak-testing. When this is done, remember that there is a difference in the specific gravities of flammable liquids and water. If water is used for hydraulic testing, the tank and all its connecting pipelines and supports should be of sufficient strength to withstand the hydraulic loading of the test. All leaks or other faults should be corrected before filling the tank.

Supports and Foundations for Above-Ground Tanks

Ideally, tanks should be supported on concrete, masonry or steel (structural steels offshore). Steel supports should be protected by material to give a fire-resistance rating of not less than two hours, although steel saddles need not be so protected if less than 30cm high at their lowest point. Supports should be designed to support the weight of the tank, all of its volume of fluid (bearing in mind the specific gravity of the fuel contained) and any residue or water/snow that may collect on it and around it in the bund. Where onshore tanks are filled from delivery vehicles, a hard-standing should be provided that takes into account the additional weight and movement of the tanker.

In order to avoid corrosion, tank supports should be designed to prevent the accumulation of water within their structures.

Supports should be designed to allow the expansion and contraction of the tank due to changes in temperature. Horizontal tanks should be secured at one end, the other being left free to move; the secured end should be the one to which the main delivery and emptying pipelines are attached. Where saddles are not welded to the tank, they should be shaped to conform to the shape of the tank shell. Every tank onshore should be securely anchored or weighted to avoid flotation due to flood water.

Tank Fittings and Connections

Where a tank is not part of a permanently-piped delivery and supply system, the tank filling line should be fitted with a suitable flange or coupling to connect with the hose delivering the fuel. The connecting point of tanks above ground should be outside the tank's bund wall. Connecting points should be in a position readily accessible to delivery vehicles (or collection vehicles for content removal) so that only one short flexible connecting hose is necessary.

Filling and emptying connections that are made and broken (plug-on and unplug hoses) should be located in the open air at a place free from all sources of ignition and not less than 2m away from any building, opening, trench, depression or drain. Spillages from connecting and disconnecting flexible hoses should be contained by a low sill, or drained to a safe place.

The discharge end of the filling line should extend into the tank below the lowest anticipated level of the liquid in order to minimise aeration and the generation of static electricity.

The discharge suction line should terminate above the bottom of the filling line so as to maintain a liquid seal.

Supports for pipework should be adequately designed, spaced and secured to suit the pipework configuration and to withstand anchorage and guide friction forces. In the case of pipe supports in the immediate vicinity of tanks, consideration should be given to their protection so as to secure a standard of fire resistance of at least two hours.

BUNDING OF STORAGE TANKS

Tanks should be surrounded by a bund to limit the spread of spillage or leakage. Alternatively, liquid may be directed to a separate collection/evaporation area, using diversion walls as necessary. Bunds may contain more than one tank (the Buncefield case study questions this) and should be designed to hold at least 110% of the capacity of the largest tank within the bund, making allowance for the space occupied by other tanks. In exceptional cases, where there is no risk of pollution or hazard to the public, this figure may be reduced to 75%.

Immediate lower bunds may be used to divide tanks into groups to contain small spillages and to minimise the surface area of any spillages, as this affects the maximum size of a bund fire.

Bunds should be substantially impervious to the liquid being stored, and designed to withstand the full hydrostatic head. They may be partly below ground level to help provide adequate wall strength. Impact protection, such as crash barriers and bollards, should be provided, where necessary.

The height of the bund should take account of the need to ensure adequate ventilation within the bund, ready access for fire-fighting and good means of escape. The height should not normally exceed 1.5m, although 2m can be used in some cases for large tanks. Diversion walls and immediate lower bunds should not exceed 0.5m unless there are special circumstances, such as sloping ground.

The floor of the bund should be made of concrete or other material that is resistant to the liquid being stored, and with drainage where necessary, to prevent minor spillages collecting near tanks. Stone chippings and similar materials may be used, providing the underlying ground is impervious. A suitable buried membrane can also be used, as can specially-designed systems, which use the water table to retain liquids not miscible with water. No vegetation (except short grass) or other combustible material, and no liquid containers or gas cylinders (full or empty) should be stored in the bund, or within 1m of the outside of the bund wall. Weedkiller containing sodium chlorate or other oxidising substances should not be used at storage areas or tanker stands because of the increased fire hazard.

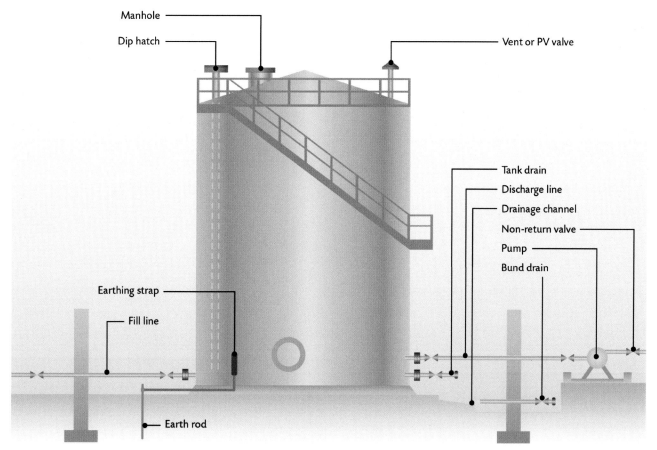

Typical Vertical Storage Tank

Safe Storage of Hydrocarbons

Means of removing surface water from the bund should be provided. If an electrically-driven pump is used, the electrical equipment should be of a type suitable for the zone in which it is used (i.e. intrinsically safe).

If a bund drain is used, it should have a valve outside the bund wall, with a system of work in force to ensure the valve remains closed, and preferably locked, except when water is being removed. Surface water from bunds where flammable liquids not miscible with water are stored should be routed through an interceptor, to prevent flammable liquids entering the main drainage system. For liquids miscible with water, special drainage systems may be required.

Loss of containment of hydrocarbon storage tanks can also have significant environmental consequences. Uncontrolled releases or leaks can enter surface-water drainage systems and cause water pollution, with subsequent environmental damage. They can also result in land contamination, with the risk of harm to human health.

If tanks are not effectively bunded then stored materials can:

- Soak into the ground, where they can pollute groundwater or contaminate land.
- Enter open drains or loose-fitting manhole covers.
- Contaminate springs, wells or boreholes.
- Contaminate watercourses, lakes and coastal waters.

FILLING OF TANKS

There is a number of issues to consider when filling tanks, the most obvious being the **suitability** of the tank, taking into consideration the type of tank, materials of construction, its size (holding capacity), location, method of filling, etc. It must be **undamaged**, with no leaks.

Once satisfied that the tank is suitable, it must be inspected to ensure that it is **empty and clean**, especially if it is to contain a different substance than previously. If not, then the previous content must be established. Mixing incompatible substances can lead to uncontrolled chemical reactions. When dealing with volatile substances it may be necessary to have the tank de-gassed and certificated 'clean' before it is filled.

The **method** of filling also has safety implications. The most common methods are:

- 'Top' filling - achieved by means of a filling valve arrangement (usually gravity-fed) through the top of the tank; more often used with smaller tanks and containers.
- 'Bottom' filling - the substance is delivered into the tank under pressure through a closed pipeline (the common method for larger tanks and road tankers).

Both these systems have some degree of risk associated with them. Top filling can create 'splash', which can contaminate the surrounding area as well as aerating the substance and creating a large electrostatic charge. It will allow the escape of vapours. While bottom filling through a closed system alleviates the problem of vapour escape, the pressure under which the substance is delivered can cause problems unless the container is designed to be pressurised, and any pressure venting and relief devices are functioning properly.

Regardless of filling method, care must be taken to avoid **overfilling**. The consequences of overfilling are potentially enormous, with uncontrolled contamination of the environment, release of vapours, and therefore vapour-cloud formation, fire and explosion. The tank must be large enough to accept the volume being put into it and the delivery suitably monitored and supervised. Bunding and spill kits should be available in case of spillage.

Suitable level-monitoring equipment should be built into the tank that will detect levels exceeding pre-set limits, and should then alarm (and, ideally, shut down).

The proper **marking** of tanks and containers is also important, as unmarked or incorrectly marked tanks can lead to tragic accidents.

> **TOPIC FOCUS**
>
> **Reducing Risks When Filling Tanks**
>
> Additional measures to take to reduce the risks associated with the filling of tanks:
>
> - Carry out a risk assessment.
> - Closely control all ignition sources (eliminate as far as possible).
> - Train and supervise all personnel involved with tank filling.
> - Identify and segregate (if possible) empty and full tanks.
> - Examine all tanks for damage.
> - Display suitable signs and notices.
> - Ensure availability of suitable fire-fighting equipment.

PRESSURISED AND REFRIGERATED VESSELS

Hydrocarbon gases can be converted to liquids for ease of storage or transport.

Liquefied natural gas (LNG) is liquefied close to the production facilities and transported in specially-designed cryogenic (low temperature) sea vessels or road tankers to a LNG regasification terminal for storage and delivery to a pipeline system.

Liquefied petroleum gas (LPG) can be liquefied by moderately increasing the pressure, or by reducing the temperature. Refrigerated storage can be used by gas suppliers to store large volumes of LPG. However, the main form of LPG storage is in special tanks known as 'pressure tanks'. These vessels will have very thick wall sections and are designed to withstand immense pressures exerted by the gas inside. They are more likely to be cylindrical or spherical in shape.

LPG vessels have a fire-resistance rating, and may have walls up to 15cm steel thickness, with pressure relief at the top, designed to vent off excess pressure to prevent rupture of the vessel. It is good practice to separate LPG vessels from others (unless together in a dedicated 'tank farm').

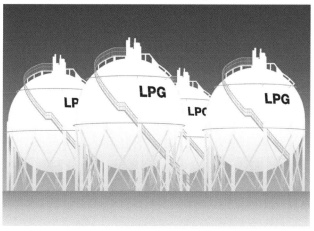

A Spherical Vessel for Storing Liquefied Gas

MORE...

You can find diagrams of the safety features of an LPG sphere and the water draw-off and sampling connections on slides 7-10 and 7-11 of the presentation *Safety Considerations in the Design of LPG Storage Vessels* by Bejoy Bharatiya at www.gpa-gcc-chapter.org/PDF/5th/Process-Safety-Considerations-Design-LPG-Pressure-Storage-Vessels.pdf

LOSS OF CONTAINMENT AND CONSEQUENCES

Jet Fires and Pool Fires

Jet fires (or spray fires) are turbulent diffusion flames that result from the combustion of a fuel that is under continuous release. The release is usually, under some momentum, jetted or sprayed in a particular direction (or directions, depending on the number of release points). Jet fires can be fuelled by gas, two-phase flashing liquids and pure liquid releases.

Jet fires present a significantly high risk of major accidents, particularly on offshore installations. The high temperatures of burning fuels sprayed onto surfaces can lead to structural failures and failure of pipework and vessels involved, which can lead to escalation of the problems.

The properties of jet fires will depend on the:

- Composition of the fuel.
- Conditions under which it is released.
- Rate at which it is released.
- Direction(s) of its release.
- Weather, in particular wind conditions at the time of release.

There will be significant differences between low and high-velocity releases, the former being often wind-affected sooty flames similar to pool fires, while high-velocity gas releases are less buoyant and cleaner fires.

Also significant will be the confinement conditions – confined and unconfined jet fires will have different effects. Releases of crude oil or mixed fuels when in contact with surfaces will have different heat fluxes, and, in confinement, all jet-fire temperatures will be carried through structures much more easily than when unconfined and being weathered and wind-blown. Confined jet fires will also have higher risks associated with smoke, thermal decomposition products and carbon (CO and CO_2) content.

Water in fuel can have some significance, particularly as fields reach their maturity and fuels naturally carry more water. This may result in more unstable jet fires. If the fire is unconfined a flame may be extinguished before the fuel supply can be shut off, resulting in a potential for explosion.

Design of installations will take into account the potential length of jet-fire flames so that adjacent buildings and structures can be spaced safely, and safety measures can be enhanced in potentially affected areas.

Safe Storage of Hydrocarbons

Pool fires are turbulent diffusing fires that burn above a horizontal pool of vaporising hydrocarbon fuel where the fuel has no or very little initial momentum (i.e. it is not, or hardly moving). The rate of pool-fire burning is the same whether the pool-fire fuel is on water or steel. Outdoor fires will be well ventilated (combustion controlled by the fuel) but enclosed fires may become under-ventilated (combustion controlled by the ventilation), and may be either static or 'running' fires. Again, they carry a significant risk of offshore major accidents, particularly where the installation has large amounts of liquid hydrocarbon fuels in process.

Heavy hydrocarbon fuels tend to burn 'messily', producing large amounts of smoke, while fuels such as LNG burn cleanly, with little smoke.

One danger, particularly with ventilation-controlled pool fires is the threat they pose to escape routes on offshore installations, because of the large flames produced.

Hydrocarbon Vapour Clouds

Hydrocarbon vapour clouds arise from releases of hydrocarbon fuels.

Mechanisms of Vapour-Cloud Explosions and Fire Spread

Explosions may occur from a physical or mechanical change or from a chemical reaction. An explosion can occur without a fire, such as the failure through over-pressure of a steam boiler or a compressed air receiver.

- In **detonation** the combustion propagates at supersonic velocity and the principal heating mechanism of the mixture is shock compression.

- In a **deflagration**, the combustion process is the same as in the normal burning of a gas mixture, the combustion zone propagates at subsonic velocity and the pressure build-up is slow.

Whether detonation or deflagration occurs in a gas-air mixture (i.e. a hydrocarbon vapour cloud) depends on various factors, including the concentration of the mixture and the source of ignition. Unless confined or ignited by a high-intensity source (a detonator), most materials will not detonate.

TOPIC FOCUS

The principles and effects of vapour-cloud explosions are:

- Vapour concentration, confined within a tank, vessel (or building) increases until it is above the Lower Explosive Limit (LEL).

- Unconfined as a release of large quantities into the open air:

  - A vapour cloud at a concentration within the explosive limits may travel some distance;

  - Dispersal may reduce the concentration below the LEL.

- Vapour-cloud explosions may arise from vaporisation of a release of liquefied gas from a ruptured vessel or pipeline.

- Explosions may be ignited by an ignition source of greater energy than the minimum ignition energy for the vapour cloud.

- Effects may be overpressure, fire, explosion and resulting debris as airborne missiles.

GLOSSARY

EXPLOSION

A sudden and violent release of energy, causing a pressure-blast wave. The shock wave decreases as the energy of the explosion is absorbed in the atmosphere. Most of the damage is done by the shock wave.

BOILING LIQUID EXPANDING VAPOUR EXPLOSIONS (BLEVE)

These explosions result from a **sudden release of vapour, containing liquid droplets**, due to the **rupture of a storage vessel** that contains a substance that is above its atmospheric boiling point, such as propane. These substances are generally stored in liquid form, but have a gaseous vapour on top of the liquid occupying the remaining volume of the storage vessel.

Following rupture:

- The vapour above the liquid rapidly escapes, lowering the pressure inside the vessel.
- Loss of pressure causes the liquid to boil violently, causing further large amounts of vapour to escape.
- Escaping vapour generates a wave of overpressure – an explosion – which can destroy the storage vessel and send debris over a large area.

BLEVEs may also be caused by a fire near the storage vessel:

- Heating the contents and rapidly increasing pressure.
- Eventually causing the safety relief valve to blow, releasing gas and reducing the volume of liquid inside the vessel available to absorb the heat of the external fire.
- Allowing the metal above the liquid level to absorb more heat and weaken.
- The vessel fails with the remaining contents boiling rapidly, discharging from the vessel, sending debris from the vessel into the air, and the resultant vapour cloud finding an ignition source, with further explosion.

A common type of BLEVE involves LPG (liquefied petroleum gas) stored under pressure in metal storage vessels. Once a fire impinges on the shell above the liquid level the vessel usually fails within 10 to 20 minutes. In the case of a BLEVE involving a flammable material, the major consequences are, in decreasing order of importance:

- Thermal radiation from the resultant fireball.
- Fragments (debris) being produced when the vessel fails.
- A blast wave produced by the expanding vapour liquid.

A BLEVE of a propane sphere of 15m in diameter could cause damage as far away as 4500m, and radiation damage and fragment damage would each extend to around 1000m. Significant damage to equipment and buildings from radiation is possible. Wooden structures may be ignited if the radiant heat density at the structure's location exceeds the threshold value for ignition of wood. Severe damage from fragmentation can be expected in the area where 50% or more of the fragments may fall (typically about 100m from the exploding vessel).

The effects of multiple BLEVEs are illustrated by the refinery fire at **Feyzin, eastern France**, on 4 January 1966. In attempting to drain off an aqueous layer from a propane storage sphere, a temporarily blocked valve allowed liquid propane to gush out. The resulting vapour cloud found a source of ignition and enveloped a storage sphere in a fierce fire. The heat from the fire caused over-pressurisation of the sphere, operation of the relief valve, and subsequent ignition of escaping vapour.

The LPG tank farm where the sphere was located contained eight propane and butane spheres, and when the fire service arrived on site it concentrated on cooling the remaining spheres rather than cooling the burning sphere. About 90 minutes after the initial leakage the burning sphere ruptured, resulting in a fireball, which killed and injured firemen and spectators. Flying missiles broke the legs of an adjacent sphere, which initiated a BLEVE. Three further spheres toppled due to the collapse of support legs, which were not adequately fire-protected and ruptured but did not explode. A number of petrol and crude-oil tanks also caught fire. The fire eventually took 48 hours to bring under control, killed 18 people, injured 81 others, and destroyed five of the storage spheres.

CONFINED VAPOUR-CLOUD EXPLOSIONS (CVCE)

CVCEs occur when a **flammable vapour cloud** ignites in a **closed space** (such as a process vessel or a building).

- Pressure builds up until the containing walls rupture.
- A relatively small amount of flammable material can lead to a significant explosion.
- Such explosions can cause considerable damage.
- CVCEs have insufficient energy to produce more than localised effects.
- For personnel close to the blast, missiles and flash-burns can result in serious or fatal injuries.

The effects of a confined vapour-cloud explosion are illustrated by the violent explosion in November 2006 at the **CAI/Arnel manufacturing facility, Danvers, USA**. The explosion and subsequent fire destroyed the facility, heavily damaged dozens of nearby homes and businesses, and shattered windows as far as two miles away. The US Chemical Safety and Hazard Investigation Board (CSB) determined that the explosion resulted from vapour released from a 2000-gallon tank of highly-flammable liquid. An open steam valve on the tank heater caused the flammable liquid to overheat and accumulate in the building production area at an explosive concentration.

Safe Storage of Hydrocarbons

Ignition of the flammable atmosphere and rapid expansion of ignited vapour inside the building created a pressure wave that shattered the rigid, brittle brick walls, disintegrated the structure and ignited large quantities of flammable liquids stored inside the building and industrial-grade nitrocellulose material stored nearby. The resultant fire burned for more than 17 hours.

UNCONFINED VAPOUR-CLOUD EXPLOSIONS (UVCE)

These explosions result from the release of a **considerable quantity of flammable gas or vapour into the atmosphere** and its **subsequent ignition**, and can cause extensive damage.

- If a large amount of volatile material is released rapidly into the atmosphere, a vapour cloud forms and disperses.
- If the cloud is ignited before it is diluted below its lower flammable limit, an unconfined vapour cloud explosion will occur.
- Shock waves and thermal radiation will result from the explosion and can have effects both on and off site.
- Effects are most pronounced when explosions involve reactive gases (such as ethylene) and least where unreactive gases (such as natural gas) are involved.

The Flixborough disaster is an example of a UVCE.

FLIXBOROUGH (UCVE)

At 4.53pm on 1 June 1974 there was an explosion at a chemical factory owned by Nypro (UK) Limited at Flixborough on Humberside, in the UK. It was equivalent to between 15 and 45 tonnes of TNT explosive. In all, 26 workers were killed and 36 injured. There were 53 reported injuries to people outside the plant and many more unreported.

Smoke rose to a height of more than 6,000ft (1,800m) so aircraft had to be diverted; some debris was found 12 miles (19.3km) away and many fires were started within a radius of 3 miles (4.8km). The 60-acre (24-hectare) site was devastated, together, as were more than 2,000 houses, factories and shops around the plant.

The plant oxidised cyclohexane, which, when heated to 155°C at a pressure of 126 psi (8.8 bar) produced caprolactan, a substance used in the manufacture of nylon. According to the chemical inventory, the plant stored large quantities of benzene, toluene, naphtha and gasoline, all of which are highly-flammable materials.

The process consisted of six reactors in series, containing a total of 120 tonnes of cyclohexane and a small amount of cyclohexanone. The final reactor in the series contained 94% cyclohexane. There was a massive leak followed by a large UVCE and fire. It was estimated that 30 tonnes of cyclohexane was involved in the explosion. The accident occurred on a Saturday; had it been a working day, casualties would have been much higher.

The chain of six reactors (retorts), each lined with stainless steel, were linked to each other by a 28-inch (711mm) diameter pipe, and there was a set of bellows at each end of the pipe to allow for expansion. Number 5 retort had developed a 6ft (1.8m) crack and, in order to take it out of use, a bypass pipe 20 inches (508mm) in diameter had been fitted between retorts 4 and 6. As each retort was 14 inches (350mm) below the next, a 'dog-leg' had to be welded into the pipe; this dog-leg was fabricated from material on the site and not from the same material as specified by the original manufacturers of the pipe.

The use of expansion joints (bellows in this case) that were incorrectly installed may have been a principal reason for the accident. This provides additional reasons not to use expansion joints (except in exceptional circumstances). When recommissioning the modified plant it was considered that the working pressure on the pipe and bellows would have been 38 tonnes; a straight pipe would have withstood this pressure, but the dog-leg pipe did not.

During the inquiry it was observed that the post of works manager was vacant and that the other chemical engineers on-site were not capable of solving engineering problems. The replacement pipe was not to the standards laid down in British Standard BS 3511:1971; also, the instructions as to how to fit the bellows had not been read. The chemical inventory exceeded the quantities allowed by the licence by 51 times.

Several new metallurgical observations were made during the inquiry: first that, in the presence of zinc, stainless steel can become embrittled and suffer cracking under heat and stress. Only small quantities of zinc are necessary and they could be found in the galvanised plating on walkways, sheets of galvanised iron and fittings; the zinc need only be near the stainless steel. Secondly, when nitrates are added to the cooling water, it can cause nitrate stress corrosion in the steel of the reactors.

A third observation was that stainless steel can produce creep cavitation when subjected to a small fierce fire, which can cause a fracture in a pipe within a matter of minutes.

Unconfined vapour-cloud explosions can have a devastating effect

Causes of the Accident

The immediate cause was determined as failure of a pipe that was replacing a failed reactor, leading to the release of a large vapour cloud of cyclohexane, which that ignited. There were, however, many contributory factors:

- The reactor failed without an adequate check on why (metallurgical failure).
- The pipe was connected without an adequate check on its strength, and on inadequate supports.
- Expansion joints (bellows) were used on each end of the pipe in a dog-leg without adequate support, contrary to the recommendations of the manufacturer.
- There was a large inventory of hot cyclohexane under pressure.
- The accident occurred during start-up.
- The control room was not built with adequate strength and was poorly sited.
- The previous works engineer had left and had not been replaced. According to the Flixborough report:

  "There was no mechanical engineer on site of sufficient qualification, status or authority to deal with complex and novel engineering problems and insist on necessary measures being taken."

- The plant did not have a sufficient complement of experienced people, and individuals tended to be overworked and liable to error.
- Management deficiencies:
  - A lack of experienced and qualified people.
  - Inadequate procedures involving plant modifications.
  - Regulations on pressure vessels that dealt mainly with steam and air and did not adequately address hazardous materials.
- A process with a very large number of hot hydrocarbons under pressure, and well above its flash point installed in an area that could expose many people to a severe hazard.

The cost of this disaster is estimated to have been in the order of £27 million for damage to the factory, and £1.6 million for the repair of shops and houses (at 1974 prices). It is a typical example of causes and sub-causes all adding up to a major disaster. By coincidence, very shortly afterwards, the **Health and Safety at Work, etc. Act 1974** came into force in the UK.

BSLR OPERATING LTD, ROSHARON, TEXAS

On 13 January 2003 a **vapour-cloud deflagration** and **pool fire** occurred, in which two workers were killed and three suffered serious burns. Two truck drivers who had just delivered gas condensate were also seriously burned in the incident.

The fire destroyed two 2,000-gallon vacuum trucks and caused serious damage to the structures of the waste liquid off-loading facility.

The fire was caused by a release of hydrocarbon vapour during the unloading of gas condensate storage-tank basic sediment and water into an open-area collection pit. Thousands of barrels of this flammable product are disposed of every year. Gas production-well operations generate this condensate liquid waste, which is collected at production gas-well sites and sold on to refineries as feed-stock. The basic sediment and water has flammability characteristics similar to petrol (gasoline).

The subsequent investigation suggested five possible ignition sources of the hydrocarbon vapour cloud:

- The diesel engine of the delivery vacuum-truck.
- The electrical system of the delivery vacuum-truck.
- Static electrical discharge from offloading the liquid waste.
- Smoking.
- The electrical wiring in the offloading facility.

Root causes were identified as:

- Failure of management to identify the potential flammability hazard of the basic sediment and water waste.
- No data sheets were provided for the delivery/off-loading trucks.
- The condensate storage tanks were not labelled with hazard information.
- There were no safety management systems in place to ensure safe handling of the waste product.
- Paperwork was not reviewed and flammability tests were not conducted on the waste.
- There was no earthing or bonding between the delivery trucks and the disposal facility.
- Unloading methods did not minimise or control vapours created during the off-loading (it was allowed to splash on open concrete pads).

Safe Storage of Hydrocarbons

Precautions to Prevent VCEs

LOCATION

Site hydrocarbon plants away from residential areas to minimise consequences if an explosion occurs.

STORAGE QUANTITIES

Keep to a minimum, especially volatile liquids under pressure, and gases.

DESIGN AND LAYOUT

Include remote isolation and shut-off valves; as much space around and between containment vessels as possible; route pipelines, cables and services together, where possible.

BUILDINGS

To be well-ventilated and resistant to the entry of vapours; minimum number of occupied buildings near plant/containment vessels; consider blast protection.

EMERGENCY AND SAFETY MEASURES

Leakage monitoring devices; sprinkler water supplies and automated alarm systems.

Pipelines

Petroleum-based products have been transported through pipelines since around 1860 (the first thought to be in Pennsylvania, USA). They are practical and economical for transporting oil, hydrocarbon products and gas, and can be overland or beneath the sea.

Most oil pipelines are built from tubes of steel or plastic with diameters from 100mm to 1200mm, and are generally buried at a depth of around 1–2m. Products flow by being pumped by intermediate pumping stations along the pipeline at speeds of between 1-6m/s.

As crude oils contain varying amounts of wax (paraffin) this can build up, especially under colder conditions, so pipelines need to be inspected and cleaned to remove build-ups. Devices with names such as 'pigs', 'scrapers' or 'go devils' (pipeline inspection gauges) are used to carry out the inspections; 'smart pigs' are also sent along the inside of pipelines to inspect and record internal conditions and remove wax deposits.

There are generally **three** classifications of pipelines:

- **Gathering pipelines** – transporting oil and gas from wells to treatment and process plant.
- **Transportation pipelines** – larger pipelines transporting oil, gas and refined products across country.
- **Distribution pipelines** – smaller pipes delivering to consumer outlets.

As well as the pipeline itself, each 'run' will be supported by field services, which include instrumentation, data and communication systems. Pumping stations and entry/recovery points (for 'pigs') will also be in place.

Instruments are placed at locations generally known as **remote terminal units** (RTUs) along the pipeline at the delivery and recovery points, as well as pump stations (or compressor houses for gas) and remote valve units.

A main control room in an operational location will control all pipeline activities and take account of all the condition monitoring (flow rates, pressure, temperatures, etc.) from the RTUs. A SCADA system in the main control room will receive all data from the RTUs and an operator will interpret this from information screens. The operator will also have controls to monitor and control functions within the pipeline delivery system.

> **TOPIC FOCUS**
>
> SCADA systems are Supervisory Control And Data Acquisition systems – industrial computer systems that monitor and control (in this case) oil and gas transportation in pipelines. They consist of:
>
> - HMI (human–machine interface), which presents data to the operator (on a screen) from which he monitors and controls the process.
> - A supervisory computer, which gathers the data from the process and sends control commands to it.
> - RTUs (remote terminal units), which are a group of interconnected sensors along the pipeline system collecting data and sending it to the supervisory system.
> - PLCs (programmable logic controllers) – field devices similar to RTUs.
> - Communication systems connecting the supervisory system to the RTUs/PLCs.

Leak Detection

Governments of countries in or across whose boundaries oil and gas pipelines pass will require a method of ensuring safety of the pipeline to protect both the asset and the local population. Oil and gas companies also have a vested interest in their asset being protected, particularly from theft of the product. It is not uncommon to find illegal tapping points in pipelines at remote locations.

To counter theft and ensure continuity of the pipeline and the supply of its product, detection systems are fitted in the pipelines that can detect changes in flow rates to as low as 2% of maximum flow. The equipment can also locate the change in flow (leak or tapping point) reasonably accurately.

There are many ways to achieve pipeline inspection, from the simplest method of 'walking the line' to satellite surveillance and location systems.

Electronically, a system known as **Computational Pipeline Monitoring** (CPM) can gather data from the pipeline that indicates pressures, flow-rates and temperatures so that fluid behaviour can be plotted for the product in the pipeline. The data are continually compared to standard data so that leaks, illegal taps or other problems (such as vandalism, arson or terrorism) can be detected.

Pipelines most at risk and the most difficult to protect are those above-ground sections that cross roads, railways, waterways, etc. where they are exposed. In many cases, electronic protection will include the use of cameras (CCTV).

It is not always the product that is subject to theft, as pipelines have systems such as cathodic pipeline protection against corrosion. Such equipment (and the security systems) is valuable, and often the target of thieves.

Pipelines most at risk and the most difficult to protect are sections that cross roads, railways, waterways, etc., where they are exposed

DECOMMISSIONING OF PLANT

Decommissioning usually occurs at the end of plant life, when plant is either no longer required, or is to be moved and recommissioned at another location, often hundreds or even thousands of miles away. Such decommissioning of hydrocarbon product plant has the extra problems associated with the product itself, and its hazardous nature.

There is immense cost associated with plant decommissioning (not even considering later transportation costs to other locations), and this has to be the first consideration in a decommissioning plan. Building the installation in the first place is a much more straightforward process than taking it apart after its life is over. For shut-down there is a lot of risk assessment work to detail all 'what if?' principles of the phased work, looking at, working out and costing potential problems along the way.

Once the plan has been put together, the first stage is **decontamination** of the existing facility, involving emptying all process equipment and vessels, pipelines, etc. and cleaning and possibly chemically treating them. Both internal and external surfaces of all installation structures and equipment will have been (potentially) exposed to contaminants, so will all have to be cleaned. Decontamination should set out to:

- Remove contaminants and reduce occupational health risks from exposure to those decommissioning the plant.
- Salvage the equipment and maintain its usability as far as possible.
- Clean up and restore the site environmentally.

Usually, freely available water and compressed air are the preferred cleaning methods, but in cases of heavy contamination (solid product residues, remains of liquids and vapours or aerosols) then steam, caustic cleaning and the use of detergents may be necessary. Alternatively, chemical treatment may be required.

Decontamination will usually take place in stages, and can often run into the second phase of decommissioning, which is dismantling.

Dismantling is also done in stages, so some of the plant and equipment may need to be dismantled before it can be decontaminated effectively. After decontamination, further dismantling may break the equipment down further into component parts for packaging and transportation.

Much of the equipment that has been cleaned and dismantled may require the application of protective coatings or packaging, especially where it may lie at a depot for a period of time before transportation and/or after arrival before being used at another location.

In cases where the plant and equipment are not required or not deemed fit for re-location or re-use, they will have to be **disposed of**. Such equipment will still need the same level of decontamination, but not the same care in dismantling if it is only to be scrapped later.

Safe Storage of Hydrocarbons

Disposal will include the disposal of any contaminants that have been collected during the decontamination process. These are likely to be hazardous in nature and must be packaged, labelled and properly disposed of according to local or national hazardous-substances regulations.

Significant Factors for Offshore Decommissioning

Within the offshore decommissioning regulatory framework there are four significant considerations, which must be balanced:

- Health and safety.
- Environmental impact.
- Technical feasibility.
- Cost-effectiveness.

Lessons Learned

From past experience (particularly in the USA) decommissioning is considered a process rather than a construction project.

- **Expect the unexpected** – drawings do not always match what is being taken apart, giving unexpected technical problems. Often, it has been found that equipment and services are not available when needed, and the weather plays an unfriendly part.
- **Time is important** – understand what is to be done before doing it and don't let outside influences rush things.
- **You don't have to bring everything ashore**.
- **Maintain a balance** between costs of decommissioning, the technology used, safety, the environment and how it is managed.
- **Consider members of the public and their opinions** and incorporate their concerns as far as possible – their beliefs are based on values and morals, not science and technology.

Securing Old Oil and Gas Wells

This relies on pre-planning to ensure the protection of the environment. You should obtain all relevant site information that may allow re-use of the installation. Evaluate the marine environment around the platform to see how decommissioning might affect it.

Finance is important – the decommissioning agent must know the current costs of the project, including plugging the well and abandoning the location (P & A costs).

Explore various disposal methods so that the best, most effective and safest method is chosen. This will include selecting the most appropriate contractors to do the work.

Decommissioning of Topside Production Equipment

Removal and disposal of topside facilities is a main part of the decommissioning process. It involves removal of the deck-support structures, drilling decks and plant, processing and transportation of oil and gas (pipelines) and the services, welfare and accommodation facilities. They vary in size and complexity, so different methods must be considered. We have already seen

that decommissioning is less straightforward than construction, and cleaning (decontamination) is all important, whether re-use or disposal is considered. Re-use should be a first choice, and health and safety and environmental impacts are important.

Removal may be achieved by:

- Taking the rig down in one piece.
- Removing it in modules.
- Taking it apart in reverse order to its construction.
- Taking it apart in unrelated small units.

Disposal may involve:

- Refurbish and re-use (preferred).
- Scrap and recycle.
- Disposing of the materials in landfill.

Removal and Disposal of Deck and Jacket Structures

Deck packages can often be removed in modules, as they were installed. This requires taking them apart and the use of lifting vessels to lift and load the modules onto transportation vessels.

The big decision here is how much of the jacket structure to remove – how much can be left where it is? The structure that supports the platform (the jacket) from the sea-bed will have been in place for many years, and will have developed a marine eco-system of its own. If left intact it may present a hazard to marine transport, but left partially intact could provide marine recreation areas (especially close to shore), while still retaining some of its under-sea eco-systems. The sea-bed structures may be particularly difficult to remove without considerable eco-damage so may be best left where they are.

Removal and disposal of topside facilities is a main part of the decommissioning process

Pipeline and Power-Cable Decommissioning

Pipelines of a size ranging from 100mm to 500mm will be in place to transport the oil or gas onshore and others used for process and service water. There will be environmental as well as technical issues with their removal.

The most appropriate method of removing the pipelines depends on:

- Locations and depths at which they are buried.
- Water depth along the route of the pipe.
- Any other nearby pipelines or marine structures and environmental considerations, e.g. the nature of the sea-bed (hard or soft, etc.), location of kelp beds, or other marine flora, etc.

So that power-generation emissions are reduced, many installations may be served by onshore power cables, which will also be considered for removal, although it is usual to leave cables rather than use large winch units to drag the whole cables ashore, or up onto a service support vessel.

In both cases, work will be required along the whole length ('alignment') of the pipes and cables, and not just in the vicinity of the platform.

Site Clearance and Verification

This is where all remaining sub-surface structures, debris from the platform and its operations (debris not intentionally dumped overboard), and sea-bed disturbances are considered for clean-up. Unless it is considered a major operational loss or environmental risk, these sea-bed items are usually left alone, in many cases actually enhancing the value of the artificial habitat they have created.

Regulations and the terms of lease of the platform location may require that it is left in a condition that will not endanger or interfere with other uses. The amount of time the platform has been in place and how much debris has accumulated on the sea floor will determine the effort needed where clean-up and removal is required.

Decommissioning and Removal of Onshore Facilities

Most offshore platforms will have a number of on-shore support facilities that are part of the total installation, such as oil and gas storage facilities (above and below-ground tanks), marine terminals, pipelines, etc. Decommissioning and disposal of these has to be considered at the same time as the platform.

Onshore facilities are more visible and easily accessible than those offshore and will therefore have to be restored as close to their original condition as possible.

Onshore removal is also a series of steps, similar to those required offshore – draining and decontamination before dismantling and disposal. Here, though, there may be additional problems of contaminated-land issues.

Environmental Issues

AIR-QUALITY ISSUES

The considerations here are the impact that removal, disposal and abandonment will have on the air quality in the area in which it is carried out. The longer the project, the more likely air quality will suffer, and the longer it will take to recover.

EFFECTS ON COMMERCIAL AND RECREATIONAL FISHERIES

During the process of decommissioning, commercial and recreational fishing may have to be suspended or restricted in the working areas. Sea-traffic routes may need to be diverted.

Once decommissioning is complete, considerations such as how much structure can be left, etc. will be determined to some extent by the continuation of fishing activities. There will be issues such as remaining shallow-water structures causing snagging to nets, and the eco-systems and marine habitats formed by the debris and structures in the platform location.

FISHERIES IMPACTS OF EXPLOSIVES USED IN PLATFORM SALVAGE

While the deck and jackets can be taken down mechanically, explosives are used on legs and pilings, usually to sub sea-bed levels. This often has a negative impact on marine life, especially fish.

EFFECTS OF DECOMMISSIONING ACTIVITIES ON MARINE LIFE

Oil and gas platforms create sea-bed artificial substrate, which develop their own marine life communities. Consideration should be given to the 'artificial reef' (closest to the sea-bed) formed by the abandoned structures and debris – this should be left alone, where possible, so the habitat can continue.

Safe Storage of Hydrocarbons

MANAGEMENT OF SIMULTANEOUS OPERATIONS

> **GLOSSARY**
>
> **SIMULTANEOUS OPERATIONS (SIMOP)**
>
> A term used mainly offshore where there is a potential clash of activities that have safety and operational implications.

The areas where clashes of activities may occur can be production and process differences, such as on multi-wellhead sites, or where operations for drilling and recovery of oil, gas, etc. run alongside each other. The term is also applied to vessel operation in support of offshore installations, such as diving vessels, lifting vessels, and the use of fixed and floating production platforms, etc. SIMOPs also often involve the activities of different contractors or companies at the same location, at the same time.

SIMOPS can occur because of:

- Contractor activities in the same location at the same time.
- Process-failure responses, such as after hydrocarbon releases, fire or explosion.
- Interference between platform and vessel operations.
- Maintenance clashes on the same plant or area at the same time by different teams.
- Weather or environmental impacts.

Where SIMOPs are identified, those who will be involved should initially meet to draw up a plan of operation, taking into account all separate activities and their impact on other work. The meeting should appoint one person to be responsible during the operations, such as the Offshore Installation Manager, or the Principal Contractor.

An agenda should identify the nature of all operations to be carried out: who, in each party, will be responsible for what; how the liaison between each party will be achieved; the time allowed for each operation. A risk assessment should be carried out for the project.

When this is done, each party involved in the simultaneous operations should put together their own file, which summarises the work in their area. This will include:

- An overall summary of the work as a step-by-step procedure (method statement).
- Drawings required by, or applicable to the work.
- Asset lists for the work.
- Constraints identified for each activity.
- An organisation chart identifying key personnel.
- A description of the main hazards identified in the operations (taken from the risk assessment already carried out).
- A summary of the control measures to be applied.
- A procedure covering management of change for any deviation in the laid-down plan.
- All safety evacuation and escape plans.
- Where vessels may be involved, or 'top-deck' operations carried out, weather limitations that will be applied.
- Communication methods for the operation.
- Contingency plans and emergency responses.

Once this and the risk assessments are in place, a **review meeting** should be held to determine the way in which the SIMOPs are to be controlled, including a hazard identification and risk assessment, and consideration for any clashes of activity that may arise.

From this, a complete hierarchy of controls will be established, and it will determine the roles and responsibilities of all involved in the operations, lines of reporting and control.

Interface documents must be established that cover all of the work to be done that is applicable to all parties involved in the operation, containing information from each party's documents.

Once established, a **pre-operations briefing** will summarise the information, ensuring all roles and responsibilities are known. Daily meetings should take place during the work and there should be regular communication between all parties involved.

One single **permit-to-work** system should operate, and be co-ordinated through one controller.

When the simultaneous operations are completed, a **close-out process** should be followed that will objectively review the activities carried out, and use the information in a 'lessons learned' manner for future projects.

Meetings and good communication contribute to successful simultaneous operations

REVISION QUESTIONS

11. What was thought to be the main cause of the tank fires at Buncefield?

12. What is the main purpose of having a floating roof in a fuel storage tank?

13. What types of fluids should be stored in a fixed-roof tank?

14. (a) What is the purpose of a bund around fuel storage tanks, and how is it generally sized?

    (b) What contradictory questions arose from the Buncefield incident regarding bunding of tanks?

15. Describe the two methods of filling tanks, and identify the circumstances where they would each be used.

16. What are the three stages of plant decommissioning?

(Suggested Answers are at the end.)

Fire Hazards, Risks and Controls

LIGHTNING

Lightning is an example of a major static electrical discharge. It is thought that initial charge separation is associated with contact between ice particles within storm clouds. Generally, charges occur in areas of low electrical conductivity, where there are few charges moving in the surroundings. A flow of neutralising charges may result from neutral atoms and molecules in the air being torn apart, then forming as separate positive and negative charges. These travel in opposite directions as an electric current, which neutralises the original accumulation of charge.

A static charge in air breaks down in this way at around 10,000 volts per centimetre (10kV/cm), being more or less dependent on the humidity. The discharge superheats the air surrounding it, causing the bright lightning flash, and creates a shock wave often heard as a clicking sound. The flash of lightning is the visible static discharge coming to ground, and occurs when the air in the channel down which the discharge flows is heated to such a high temperature that it gives out incandescent light. The thunder we hear with the lightning flash is the shock wave created as the superheated air expands explosively.

Installations and plant should be protected from lightning strikes by suitable lightning-rod applications, usually fixed to the highest point on various items of plant and structures and connected to ground to dissipate energy from a strike.

THE FIRE TRIANGLE AND POTENTIAL CONSEQUENCES

The Fire Triangle

What do we need to start a fire?

The Triangle of Combustion

A combustible/flammable substance or **fuel** (wood, paper, plastics, gas, petrol, etc).

- **Oxygen** in a gas state (usually from air).
- An ignition source (or **heat**).

If the conditions are right and these three factors are present, the substance will catch fire, i.e. heat and light will be produced, accompanied by volumes of smoke and gases, which will rise away from the fire.

These three factors form the basis of the **Fire Triangle**, and all must be present to produce and sustain a fire. Take any one of the three elements away, and a fire will go out.

FUEL

Fuel consists of flammable and combustible materials, which cover all states of matter:

- Combustible solids, e.g. wood, plastics, paper/wrapping and packaging materials, soft furnishings and fabrics, and even metals, e.g. magnesium.
- Flammable solids, e.g. magnesium (in finely divided form, such as powder).
- Flammable liquids, e.g. petroleum and its derivatives, paints, solvents, oils, etc.
- Flammable gases, e.g. hydrogen, LPG, LNG, methane, etc.

AIR/OXYGEN

Although under certain unusual circumstances it is possible to produce combustion-like chemical reactions with materials such as chlorine or sulphur, it is safe to say that nearly all combustion requires the presence of oxygen. The higher the concentration of oxygen in an atmosphere, the more rapidly burning will proceed.

Whilst the most common source of oxygen is obviously from the air, in some workplaces there may also be additional sources, e.g. oxygen cylinders or substances that are oxidising agents.

HEAT

Heating a very small quantity of fuel and oxygen mixture (to a sufficient degree) is enough to start a fire. Then, since fires are by definition exothermic, the very small fire started by a tiny heat source supplies to its surroundings more heat than it absorbs, enabling it to ignite more fuel and oxygen mixture, and so on, until very quickly there is more heat available than is needed to propagate a large fire. The heat may be provided by various sources of ignition.

Classification of Fires

Fires are commonly classified into five categories, according to the fuel type. The classification is useful as the basis for identifying which extinguisher to use.

The classification system used in Europe is shown below:

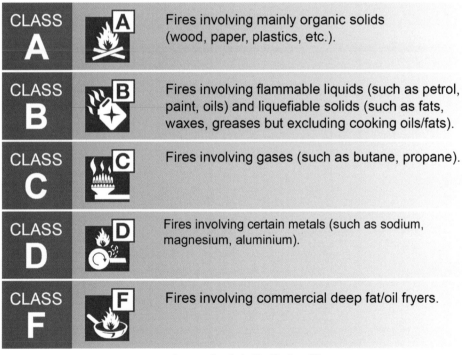

CLASS A	Fires involving mainly organic solids (wood, paper, plastics, etc.).
CLASS B	Fires involving flammable liquids (such as petrol, paint, oils) and liquefiable solids (such as fats, waxes, greases but excluding cooking oils/fats).
CLASS C	Fires involving gases (such as butane, propane).
CLASS D	Fires involving certain metals (such as sodium, magnesium, aluminium).
CLASS F	Fires involving commercial deep fat/oil fryers.

European Standard - Classification of Fires

Fire Hazards, Risks and Controls

(**Note** that there is no Class E fire. This was avoided to prevent confusion between Class E and Electricity. Electricity is not a fuel (although it can be a heat/ignition source).)

Similar classification systems exist in the United States and in Australia and Asia but with slight differences in designatory letters and with the inclusion of electrical fires as a separate class of fire. However, the key principle of classifying the fire according to its fuel source in order to specify the most appropriate extinguishing agent is common to all systems.

Explosion and Thermal Radiation: Mechanisms of Explosion and Fire Spread

HOW AN EXPLOSION/FIRE OCCURS

An explosion may occur from a physical or mechanical change or from a chemical reaction. An explosion can occur without fire, such as the failure through overpressure of a steam boiler or an air receiver.

Whether detonation or deflagration occurs in a gas-air mixture depends on various factors, including the concentration of the mixture and the source of ignition.

Unless confined or ignited by a high-intensity source (a detonator), most materials will not detonate. However, the pressure wave (blast wave) caused by a deflagration can still cause considerable damage.

Certain materials, such as acetylene, can decompose explosively in the absence of oxygen and because of this are particularly hazardous.

In basic terms, volatile molecules of the fuel are combined with oxygen to produce new compounds (combustion products). This is an oxidation reaction (see later).

Fuel does not generally spontaneously combust in air (think of coal). It requires some energy to vaporise sufficient fuel molecules and to initiate the reaction, e.g. by supplying heat. Once initiated, the heat produced by the reaction itself can supply the heat needed to sustain further vaporisation and combustion of fuel, so that the external heat source is no longer required.

Stages of Combustion

Combustion can be divided into five stages:

INDUCTION

Heat is initially supplied by an external source, which results in production of flammable vapour. These vapours mix with air above the fuel and, if sufficient energy is provided, the combustion reaction begins between the vapour and the oxygen.

IGNITION

The point of ignition is reached when the reaction becomes self-sustaining (and no longer requires an external heat source). At this stage combustion develops very quickly and there is a dramatic increase in temperature as the fire grows.

GROWTH

Once ignited, the fire may spread through direct burning, or through the typical mechanisms of heat transmission (convection, conduction or radiation). The rate, scale and pattern of growth depend on a number of factors, such as:

- Nature, form and amount of the fuel.
- Availability of oxygen (open, ventilated versus sealed containment).
- Amount of heat produced by the reaction.

STEADY STATE

After the growth period the temperature stabilises and the combustion process reaches a steady state, where the reaction between fuel and oxygen is balanced until all the fuel is consumed.

DECAY

Decay will begin when either the fuel or oxygen has been consumed. The fire will extinguish and gradually cool down. In the early stages of decay, there is still a considerable amount of heat; there is certainly enough to cause re-ignition if more fuel or oxygen is supplied. In the latter case, admission of oxygen (e.g. opening a window) into an oxygen-depleted room can result in the sudden explosive re-ignition of vapours.

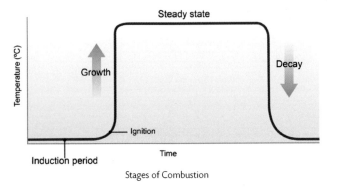

Stages of Combustion

FIRE

A combustion reaction in which fuel is converted to combustion products (smokes, fumes, gases) in the presence of oxygen. It is a rapid, self-sustaining gas-phase oxidation process, which produces heat and light. When combustion takes place in solids or liquids, it is the vapours given off that ignite rather than the solid or liquid itself.

ELECTROSTATIC CHARGES

The flow of flammable liquids inside a pipe can build up static electricity. This is generated by moving contact between dissimilar materials, such as the flammable liquid and the pipe, which causes positive and negative charges to separate and accumulate in the liquid and on the pipe. Many fuels are capable of collecting ('accumulating') charges and holding it during high velocity flow. This accumulated static electrical charge can be released (discharged) and if the discharge energy is high enough, it will ignite a fuel vapour and air mixture. The static discharge required to cause ignition will depend greatly on the flammability limits of the fuel in air mixture.

Static electricity is generated by process activities such as mixing, pouring, pumping, filtering, or agitating liquids, and the rate of generation is determined by:

- **Conductivity** – some flammable liquids have very low conductivity and will accumulate static charges.
- **Turbulence** – large flow rates, splashing or free-falling liquids greatly increase the accumulation of static charge.
- **Surface area** – filters have large surface areas and can generate much higher electrostatic charges than pipework without filtration.
- **Flow rate** – the most effective method of reducing the accumulation of static charges in piping systems is through proper pipe sizing to keep liquid velocities low.
- **Presence of impurities** – mixing any dissimilar substances with flammable liquids, such as water or rust, will increase static generation.

Although the generation of static electricity is difficult to eliminate, its rate of generation and accumulation can be reduced by:

- Control of pumping rates.
- Proper pipe sizing to keep liquid velocities low.
- Elimination of splash filling and free-fall of flammable liquids by:
    - Lowering fill velocities.
    - Directing the discharge of liquid down the side of the vessel.
    - Submerging fill pipes below the liquid level in the vessel.
- Installing filters far enough upstream of discharge points to allow adequate time for any static generated to leak away.

The biggest risk of static electrical discharge is where fuel is being transferred from one vessel to another; rather than following the fuel the charge will find an easier route and discharge to ground (to earth or another structure).

Good earthing and bonding systems will help reduce the discharge by allowing continuity through the fuelling system connections, as will conducting materials in vessel and pipework structures. In some cases, additives are available to put in the fuels to prevent or dissipate the build-up of static electrical charges.

IDENTIFYING IGNITION SOURCES

Ignition sources include:

- Open flames – matches, welding torches, etc.
- Electrical sparking sources (switches, electric motors, etc).
- Spontaneous ignition.
- Sparks from grinding or tools.
- Sparks or heat from internal combustion engines.
- Static electricity.
- Friction.
- Hot surfaces (e.g. heaters or overheating equipment).
- Sparks (arising from impact of metal tools, electrical arcing and static discharges).
- Lasers and other intense radiant-heat sources.
- Chemical reactions giving rise to heat/flame.
- Smoking.

Sparks from welding or burning are a common ignition source

Fire Hazards, Risks and Controls

Control of Vapour-Phase Explosions

A vapour-phase explosion is a sudden and violent release of energy, causing a pressure blast wave.

Investigation and analysis of the cause and consequences of vapour-phase explosions identifies the following important control principles:

- **Plant and process design and control** can reduce the risk of fire and explosion by preventing flammable concentrations of vapour developing and coming into contact with sources of ignition. In addition, isolation can stop the explosion from reaching other areas of the plant through pipes or ducts. Pressure-resistant equipment will contain an explosion. Process controls can ensure that concentrations do not exceed the lower flammable limit.
- **Structural protection** incorporated into building design can reduce the effects of a vapour-phase explosion on occupants.
- **Segregation and storage of materials** will aim to ensure that flammable substances are stored outside, in designated storage areas. If kept inside, they should be segregated from any work that is likely to produce a source of ignition.
- **Inerting** involves the partial or complete substitution of the air in an enclosed space by an inert gas and can be used very effectively to prevent explosions.
- **Explosion relief** reduces the damage from a vapour-phase explosion by either relieving the pressure generated by the explosion by means of vents, panels and bursting discs, or by suppressing the explosion through inerting.
- **Control of material quantities** limits the amount to be stored in a workroom or working area and requires justification of the need to store any particular quantity of flammable liquid within a workroom/working area. The guiding principle is that only the minimum quantity needed for frequently occurring activities, or that required for use during half a day or one shift, should be present in the workroom/working area. It is recommended that the maximum quantity stored in cabinets and bins is no more than 50 litres for extremely, highly-flammable and those flammable liquids with a flashpoint below the maximum ambient temperature of the workroom/working area; and no more than 250 litres for other flammable liquids with a higher flashpoint of up to 55°C.

- **Release can be prevented** by storing flammable liquids in a separate storage area, or in a purpose-made bin or cupboard, keeping containers closed when not in use, using safety containers with self-closing lids, dispensing liquids over a tray, and using non-flammable absorbent material to mop up spills.
- **Ignition sources can be controlled** by removing all the obvious ignition sources from the storage and handling areas for flammable liquids. Typical ignition sources include sparks from electrical equipment or welding and cutting tools, hot surfaces, open flames from heating equipment, and smoking materials.
- **Other control options** include the sensing of vapour between LEL and UEL in order to detect the formation of an explosive atmosphere, which can trigger an alarm system, or preventative actions, such as ventilation or inerting.

ZONING AND HAZARD AREA CLASSIFICATION

Hazardous area zoning classifies areas on the basis of the frequency and duration of the occurrence of an explosive atmosphere. The zones are shown below for gas/vapours, with those for dust in brackets.

ZONE 0

A place in which an explosive atmosphere consisting of a mixture of air with dangerous substances in the form of **gas, vapour or mist** is present continuously, or for long periods of time, or frequently (Zone 20 for **dust**).

ZONE 1

A place in which an explosive atmosphere consisting of a mixture of air with dangerous substances in the form of **gas, vapour or mist** is likely to occur in normal operation occasionally (Zone 21 for **dust**).

ZONE 2

A place in which an explosive atmosphere consisting of a mixture of air with dangerous substances in the form of **gas, vapour or mist** is not likely to occur in normal operation but, if it does occur, will persist for a short period only (Zone 22 for **dust**).

The zone will define the requirements for the selection of equipment to be used in the hazardous area:

- Zone 0 or Zone 20 – Category 1 equipment.
- Zone 1 or Zone 21 – Category 1 or 2 equipment.
- Zone 2 or Zone 22 – Category 1, 2 or 3 equipment.

Types of Equipment

INTRINSICALLY SAFE EQUIPMENT (TYPE 'I')

This design ensures that the energy level is insufficient to produce an incendiary spark. Two categories of intrinsically safe equipment exist: 'ia' which is more stringent as it allows for two simultaneous faults, and 'ib', which allows for only one. Only 'ia' equipment can be used (exceptionally) in Zone 0 if sparking contacts are not part of the equipment. Examples of type 'i' are instrumentation and low-energy equipment.

FLAMEPROOF EQUIPMENT (TYPE 'D')

Flameproof equipment is totally enclosed and the casing has to be robust enough to withstand internal explosions without igniting the flammable atmosphere in which the equipment is located. Examples of type 'd' equipment are motors, lighting, switchgear and portable handlamps. Due to its robust structure it is heavy and expensive. It is suitable for use in Zones 1 or 2 but is unsuitable for Zone 0.

TYPE 'E' EQUIPMENT

This equipment does not arc, spark or generate temperatures high enough to ignite a flammable atmosphere. Examples of type 'e' equipment are induction motors and transformers. Type 'e' equipment may be used in Zone 2 areas.

TYPE 'N' EQUIPMENT (NON-SPARKING)

Less stringent requirements have to be met by this category, compared with type 'e' equipment. It is intended for use in Zone 2 applications. Examples of type 'n' or 'N' equipment are some solid-state relays.

TOPIC FOCUS

Intrinsically safe electrical equipment and flameproof equipment afford protection by different means.

With intrinsically safe equipment:

- Electrical energy is restricted.
- Energy levels are insufficient to produce an incendiary spark.
- Use in Zone 0 areas is possible.
- Faults may raise energy levels.

Flameproof equipment:

- Allows an explosive mixture to enter the enclosure but the enclosure will withstand the pressure and heat of explosion and the ignition of the surrounding flammable atmosphere is prevented.
- Is not suitable for some combustible powders and dusts.
- Can be used in Zones 1 and 2.
- Requires regular maintenance to ensure continuing integrity.

REVISION QUESTIONS

17. What are the three elements that make up the fire triangle?
18. What are the five stages of combustion?
19. List the three hazard zones and the categories of electrical equipment to be used in each zone.

(Suggested Answers are at the end.)

Furnace and Boiler Operations

USE OF FURNACE AND BOILER OPERATIONS

Furnaces and boilers are used to heat water to produce steam, which is used in the oil and gas process industries for a variety of reasons, including heating and steam for turbine operation and steam washing and cleaning, as well as product recovery at wells. They are also used as a source of heat in oil and gas processing.

In a steam boiler, a fuel is ignited (such as oil, gas, etc.) to produce a flame, which heats water to boiling point. Rather than placing a flame directly beneath the boiler's water container, most modern boilers now have superheating elements. These concentrate the space in which the steam is produced, giving it greater energy.

Steam boilers use the convection principle, using the steam that collects at the top of the boiler to preheat water flowing into the boiler from the inlet tubes, ensuring that cold water does not enter the boiler, and keeping internal temperatures high.

Steam boilers fall into two common types: **closed systems**, in which unused condensed steam goes back through the system to be re-heated; or **open systems**, where the boiler vents unused steam from the system, usually requiring a continuous flow of water.

Closed and open boilers are also in two forms:

- **Firetube boilers** – (the most common type) having an outer shell (the firetube) with tubes of water inside it. Heated gases pass through the core of the firetube and heat water in the internal water tubes, which creates the steam.
- **Watertube boilers** – the simplest boiler, which has a vertical tube above the heating source. Water enters the vertical tube and is heated until it becomes steam, which then passes out through the top of the tube.

At the oil refinery crude oil is heated directly in a furnace and fractional distillation separates by boiling point the various petroleum products such as LPG, petrol, kerosene, diesel oil, fuel oil and asphalt.

HAZARDS AND RISKS OF BOILER OPERATIONS

The main hazards associated with boiler operations are:

- **Loss of pilot-gas supply** – regardless of the type of fuel used for the boiler (e.g. gas, oil, diesel, etc.) a pilot gas flame will be maintained and used to light the boiler fuel. Pilot flames are lit by an ignition transformer, the pilot in turn lighting the main flame. Atomisers are used when using liquid fuels. If the pilot flame goes out (perhaps from interruption of gas supply, or over-pressure from the main gas supply), gas powering the pilot will continue to enter the unit, causing a potential build-up of flammable/explosive gases, which can lead to boiler explosion. Flame detectors are used, located so that the pilot flame can be 'seen' at all times during operation.
- **Low tube flow** – flow of either hot water or heated air through the boiler tubes (depending on the type of boiler) must be maintained in order to control both temperature and pressure in the boiler. If tube flow reduces, heat exchange will become inefficient, causing temperature and pressure rises, which could lead to explosion.
- **Control of tube metal temperature (TMT)** – essential to ensure excessive stresses are not placed on boiler tubes during increased cycle demands. Tube temperature monitoring in the boiler furnace walls, generating tubes, superheater tubes and reheater tubes can aid with troubleshooting boiler problems, such as leakages, breaks and blockages in pressurised parts of the boiler and detecting heat-transfer reduction caused by scale build-up. Tube metal temperatures are measured during operating cycles using thermocouples welded into the tube walls.

Important to the operation of all boiler types is the management of water content within the boiler, which must be constantly monitored. Where water levels run low, extensive damage can be caused, even resulting in an explosion. Generally, water and temperature are monitored together – if water is low, an indicator is that the temperature may be too high.

Boiler explosions are a kind of BLEVE, and the pressure of steam can be extremely high; steam will require 1,600 times more space than water, meaning that one cubic metre of boiler water will expand to 1,600 cubic metres of steam in a very short time (a matter of seconds).

Before operating, all valves and switches must be checked for correct operation, and all pipe fittings and valves checked to ensure that they are clear of blockages and remain open. A low-water cut-off valve should be in place to ensure water is maintained at safe levels during operation, and regular tests should be carried out (e.g. evaporation tests) to ensure low-water cut-off functions correctly.

All dampers should be fully opened before firing the boiler, and the firebox of the boiler ventilated to remove previous unburned gases (oil fumes, fuel gas, etc.). The flame must be maintained at the correct level throughout operation to prevent flame-out or flame impingement. **Firebox explosions** happen after flame-out, usually when the firebox is hot. This can occur in gas-fuelled or gas-ignition systems if the pilot light goes out for any reason. If fuel vapours explode in the firebox it is likely to damage the pressurised tubes inside the boiler shell, leading to structural failure and steam leakage. This may then create a steam explosion.

Boilers are fitted with safety valves to prevent the pressure rising above safe pre-set limits if standard pressure valves fail to operate. These must be kept clean and free from sediment and contaminants and tested regularly.

Overfiring is having the flame too big, either because of too much fuel or poor flame adjustment. This can also lead to flame impingement. **Flame impingement** is where a flame that is used to heat the water in a boiler touches boiler surfaces, such as directly on heating coils or pipework. This can cause erosion and corrosion, cracking and failure of the materials. This should not occur within boilers, and can be prevented by:

- Ensuring the burner is always correctly adjusted.
- Tilting the burner to direct the flame away from surfaces.
- Moving the flame further away from surfaces.
- Ensuring proper flame control.

Poor water management and lack of, or incorrect, water treatment can also increase the problems of flame impingement, by allowing a build-up of sediment and other contaminants inside the tubes, which themselves add to localised heating on the inside of tubes, while flames impinge upon the outside surfaces.

In the refining process crude oil is heated in a direct-fired furnace and fed into a vertical distillation column at a pressure slightly above atmospheric and at a temperature of around 400°C, where all but the heaviest fractions flash into vapour. Although these are closed processes, there is the potential for fire and explosion if a leak or release occurs. Strict control of temperature and pressure within operating parameters is required to prevent excursions, and relief systems should be provided for overpressure.

MORE...

You can find a general overview of steam boilers and associated equipment in *'An Introduction to Steam Boilers and Steam Raising'* at:

www.cip.ukcentre.com/steam.htm

More details on the necessary fittings, accessories and controls for a boiler, such as safety valves, gauge glasses and level controls, are available at:

www.spiraxsarco.com/resources/steam-engineering-tutorials/the-boiler-house/boiler-fittings-and-mountings.asp

REVISION QUESTIONS

20. What are the two common types of boilers and the two forms of each?

21. What is 'flame impingement' and what problems are commonly caused by it?

(Suggested Answers are at the end.)

SUMMARY

This element has further explored hydrocarbon process safety. In particular, it has:

- Outlined the types of failure modes that may lead to loss of containment from hydrocarbons, such as creep, stress, cracking, thermal shock and brittle fracture.

- Explained the term 'safe operating envelope' and shown how to use the knowledge of failure modes in design and safe operating procedures.

- Discussed the types of failures that may lead to loss of containment from hydrocarbons – in particular, weld failures, and the need for regular inspection.

- Outlined the controls available to maintain safety-critical equipment, including emergency shutdown (ESD) controls and safety integrity levels (SILs) for instrumentation, blow-down facilities and flare types, and drainage systems.

- Explained the hazards, risks and controls available for safe storage of hydrocarbons offshore and onshore, including floating and fixed-roof tanks and bunding.

- Highlighted the consequences of loss of containment, such as jet and pool fires, BLEVEs, CVCEs and UVCEs.

- Discussed the protection of pipelines, the decommissioning of plant and the management of simultaneous operations (SIMOPs).

- Noted the fire hazards, risks and controls relating to hydrocarbons.

- Outlined the hazards, risks and controls available for operating boilers and furnaces.

Exam Skills

QUESTION

(a) Identify TWO non-destructive test (NDT) methods for identifying internal defects in materials.   (4)

(b) For the two methods identified, outline the advantages and disadvantages of each method.   (4)

APPROACHING THE QUESTION

- Using the system we have covered, the first thing to do is read the question carefully. You are asked to identify two NDT methods. You should structure your approach (a bullet-point list can be used to identify the methods available) and identify your two chosen methods.

- Next, consider the marks available. In this question there are eight marks; we can presume that the question awards two marks to each NDT method identified. The other four will be given as one mark each for valid advantages and disadvantages for the two methods identified.

- The question should take around eight minutes.

- Now highlight the key words. In this case, it might look like this:

  Identify TWO non-destructive test (NDT) methods for identifying internal defects in materials.

  (a) For the two methods identified, outline the advantages and disadvantages of each method.

  (b) Read the question again – make sure you understand it.

- Following this, the next stage is to develop a plan. Remember, a plan can be completed in various ways, but it could consist of the following:

SUGGESTED ANSWER

Plan

Test	Advantages	Disadvantages
Dye penetrant	Inexpensive and convenient. Superior to visual examination alone. For all non-porous materials.	Surface defects only. Defects must be open to the surface.
Magnetic particle	More sensitive than dye penetrant. Can also find sub-surface defects.	Ferrous metals only. **Cannot find defects at any significant depth**. Requires a power source.
Eddy current	Rapid detection of surface or sub-surface flaws. Can measure depth of shallow flaws.	Cannot operate close to other free surfaces, e.g. thin sheet. **Cannot find deep flaws**. Requires a power source.
Ultrasonic	Precise location of **internal** and external **defects**. Sizing of many defects possible.	Expensive equipment. Dependent on a skilled operator and a power supply.
Radiography	Permanent, pictorial, easily interpreted images obtained. Locates majority of **internal defects**.	Safety hazards (radiation). Expensive X-ray sets. Thickness limits (more so with X-rays). Power supply needed. Needs access to both sides.

Now have a go at the question yourself.

Exam Skills

POSSIBLE ANSWER BY EXAM CANDIDATE

(a) Two non-destructive testing (NDT) methods that will detect internal defects are ultrasonics, using sound waves to penetrate into a material, and radiography, using gamma or X-rays to penetrate through the material, leaving a pictorial image on a film.

(b) The advantages of ultrasonics are that it can detect the precise location of internal defects and can size many defects, too. Its disadvantages are that it is expensive, requires a skilled operator and a power supply.

The advantages of radiography are that it can locate the majority of internal defects and it gives a permanent pictorial record of the defect. Disadvantages are the radiation risk to operators and others in the testing area, and there are limits to the thickness it can accurately penetrate. It needs a power supply and access to both sides of the material tested.

REASONS FOR POOR MARKS ACHIEVED BY CANDIDATES IN EXAM

- Not answering the question at all. If you do not attempt all questions required you cannot get any marks.
- Not following a structured approach: remember, the question required TWO methods to be identified and one valid advantage and disadvantage for each for the eight marks.
- The question asked you to identify, so a list of the two NDT methods would not gain maximum marks.
- Giving lots of other information not relevant to the question, or identifying surface or sub-surface methods when internal were asked for.

FIRE PROTECTION AND EMERGENCY RESPONSE

ELEMENT
4

LEARNING OUTCOMES

On completion of this element, you should be able to demonstrate understanding of the content by applying what you have learnt to familiar and unfamiliar situations. In particular, you should be able to:

1 Outline appropriate control measures to minimise the effects of fire and explosion in the oil and gas industries.

2 Outline the principles, procedures and resources for effective emergency response.

Contents

Fire and Explosion in the Oil and Gas Industries

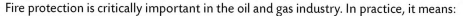

KEY INFORMATION

Fire protection is critically important in the oil and gas industry. In practice, it means:

- Detection of leaks (gas, vapour, liquid and oil mist).
- Detection of fire and its products (heat, smoke).
- Installation of passive fire protection, such as spray-applied cement-based coatings.
- Installation and use of active fire protection, such as water/foam deluge, sprinklers, monitors and extinguishers.

LEAK AND FIRE DETECTION SYSTEMS

These systems comprise detectors for gas/vapour, flame, heat and smoke, which continuously monitor the area. Routinely, they also raise the alarm on detection and may then initiate control action, such as emergency shutdown.

General considerations of these systems include:

ADEQUATE NUMBER OF DETECTORS AND LOCATION

The ability to detect may be defeated by local air flows and the density of the gas. You will remember from Element 1 that some gases, like LPG and hydrogen sulphide, are denser than air and so will tend to collect at lower levels. A detector placed at high level is unlikely to detect such a leak early enough. Similarly, local air flows may take the path of a leaking gas/vapour away from the detector. Once again, the detector will not 'see' the leak.

MAINTENANCE/TESTING

Many systems have failed because of fouling, corrosion, etc. A fault-detection circuit should be incorporated.

UNINTERRUPTIBLE POWER SUPPLY

In the event of power failure, the protection is maintained.

MANUAL BACK-UP

The system is supplemented with manual call points.

MINIMISATION OF FALSE ALARMS

If the detector initiates some control action (such as a shut down), to reduce the potential for false alarms a voting system can be incorporated (i.e. several detectors are required to activate to set off the alarm and subsequent control action), but this will require a higher density of detectors. Typically voting systems may be set to trigger if 2 out of 3 detectors are activated, but it depends on the perceived level of risk. In some cases, it can be 2 out of 16 or 3 out of 75.

ZONING

Detectors are often wired together into groups/zones (just like alarms), so that they trigger a zone alarm on the fire-alarm panel.

Leak Detection

Gas/vapour detectors can be used to detect leaks such as those from pump seals. They can also be installed in bunds surrounding flammable-liquid storage vessels to detect loss of containment from tanks. The detectors can be specific to the substance or range of substances being detected. It is important to make sure the detector is calibrated for the hydrocarbons being used. It may be appropriate to have a tiered approach, whereby detection of low levels initiates investigation rather than shut-down.

Some instruments are able to detect liquid hydrocarbon leaks (they work on the basis of conductivity measurement variation, when oil floats on water in a sump). Liquid leaks can also be detected visually using dedicated CCTV systems coupled with auto-sensing software.

Oil-mist detectors (optical-beam type) may also be necessary. Oil mist is generated from leaks of pressurised hydrocarbon liquids (e.g. through pin holes). The mist generated is flammable but, it appears, is not consistently detected by standard gas/vapour detectors.

Fire and Explosion in the Oil and Gas Industries

Fire Detection

Fire detectors are broadly divided into those for smoke, heat or flame.

SMOKE DETECTORS

There are two basic types (ionisation and optical).

- **Ionisation types** use a radioactive compound (typically americium-241, which emits alpha particles) to ionise the air in a chamber; this generates a small current, which is reduced when smoke particles enter the device. This is what triggers the alarm.
- **Optical types** work either on the principle of **scattering** (smoke scatters light from a light source held within a chamber so that it falls onto a photoelectric cell and triggers the alarm), or **obscuration** (smoke obscures a light beam, reducing its intensity at a photoelectric cell).

HEAT DETECTORS

These are generally slower to respond than other detectors (because of thermal lag). They either contain **fusible** links (of metal alloy or plastic which melt in the fire, triggering the alarm) or work on the **expansion** of either metal, liquid or air (pneumatic type). They can be made to activate: at a fixed temperature; or be sensitive to the rate of rise of temperature; or both.

There are two basic configurations of heat detectors:

- **Spot** (or **point**) **type** – the commonly seen individual units.
- **Line type** – comprise cables, which are able to detect temperature variations at any point along its length.

FLAME DETECTORS (UV/VISIBLE/IR)

These detect either UV, visible or IR radiation emitted from the fire. It is essential to maintain line of sight from the detector to the potential flame source – often, they are obscured by equipment and stored materials.

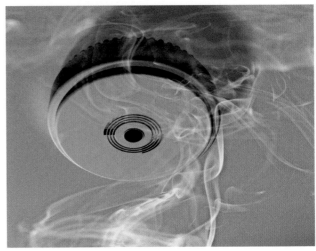

Smoke detector

MORE...

For more information on BS EN ISO 13702:1999 visit www.iso.org

Fire & Gas System

HAZARD	TYPE OF DETECTOR		TYPICAL APPLICATION
FIRE	Heat	Pneumatic	Process, wellhead utilities
		Electric	Turbine hoods, workshops, stores, engine rooms, process, wellhead utilities
	Flame		Process, wellhead utilities, generators, gas turbines
	Smoke		Control rooms, electrical rooms, computer rooms, accommodation
			Air intakes to temporary refuges (TR) and control stations
FLAMMABLE GAS			Process, wellhead utilities areas*, engine rooms* Air intakes
OIL MIST			Enclosed areas handling low GOR (gas/oil ratio) liquid hydrocarbons
	Manual call point		All areas, escape routes, muster points, TRs
	NOTE: Process areas include drilling areas. *Only for rooms containing essential safety systems		

Table showing some typical applications of leak and fire detectors (Based on Table C2 of BS EN ISO 13702:1999, Petroleum and natural gas industries – Control and mitigation of fires and explosions on offshore production installations – Requirements and guidelines)

PASSIVE FIRE PROTECTION

Passive fire protection (PFP) is fire protection that is typically used:

- On **fire barriers** (i.e. structures, such as walls, that are designed to stop fire transmission between different protected areas/compartments).
- To protect **load-bearing structures** (like columns) supporting key areas, such as accommodation blocks.
- To protect **critical equipment/components**.

Essentially, PFP protects the structure to which it is applied, stopping (or at least drastically reducing) the heat and smoke from destroying its structural integrity (especially important for evacuation routes) and limiting spread to other parts (in the case of fire walls, dividing an area into fire-resisting compartments – a technique known as 'compartmentation'). The protection afforded by PFP is only temporary (typically 30 minutes to 2 hours).

PFP can come in many forms:

PREFORMED (E.G. BOARDS, PANELS, CLADDING, WALL LININGS, PIPE SHELLS)

These are often inorganic fibres (e.g. glass, mineral or ceramic) mixed with either an organic polymer or cement binder. They can also be made from epoxy-resin intumescent materials, or Portland cement.

PREFABRICATED

This is a fire-resisting structure that has been prefabricated off-site for on-site erection. Some fire barriers/walls/partitions are made in this way – prefabricated sections bolted together on site. A fire door is another example.

SPRAY COATINGS

Such as epoxy resin-based intumescents, cement-based plasters and endothermic coatings. Spray-applied coatings are typically used on columns, beams, bulkheads, fire walls, flare booms and vessel supports.

ENCLOSURES

These are essentially fire-resisting boxes or trunking placed around critical components (such as emergency shut-down valves) and systems.

SEALS/SEALANTS

A classic example is the intumescent door seal, placed around a fire door, designed to prevent the passage of fire and smoke and activated by heat. Sealants are also commonly used to plug gaps around holes where services pass through a fire compartment wall. In such cases, they are called 'fire stopping'.

FLEXIBLE JACKETS

These wrap around a structure and are often based on woven glass fibre. A range of flexible PFP jackets is available, which can be adapted to many situations, including enclosing equipment, supports, lining bulkheads (i.e. walls/partitions on ships, offshore platforms), etc. These have the advantage that they can easily be removed for maintenance.

> **GLOSSARY**
>
> **INTUMESCENT**
> A product which expands when it comes into contact with heat.
>
> **ENDOTHERMIC**
> Reactions that take place with the absorption of heat.

Fire and Explosion in the Oil and Gas Industries

Nature of the Fire

The nature of the fire obviously has a big effect. There are three basic types of relevant fire:

- Hydrocarbon jet fires.
- Hydrocarbon pool fires.
- Those involving cellulosics (combustibles such as wood, paper, etc).

Hydrocarbon pool fires achieve a higher maximum temperature and a greater rate of temperature rise than cellulosic fires. The ability of passive fire protection to withstand these fires is reasonably predictable (standard tests exist for this), so passive fire protection can be selected with reasonable certainty in these cases.

Hydrocarbon jet fires are a different matter – the effects vary widely with hydrocarbon type, pressure and flow rate. As a result, you need to establish the likely fire scenarios (type and how long they are likely to last, typically up to 2 hours) before selecting passive protection that can withstand them. Given the harsh conditions experienced offshore, the passive protection also needs to be resistant to weathering.

The presence of LPG (and similar vaporising liquids) will mean the passive fire protection needs to be resistant to thermal shock (extreme cold followed by extreme heat). In addition, the materials should be resistant to the effects of explosion.

	PROTECTION CRITERIA	
	SURFACE TEMPERATURE (°C)	MINIMUM PROTECTION PERIOD
Riser sections	< 200[a]	60[b]
Riser supports	< 400	60[b]
Riser topside SDV (shutdown valve)	< 200	60[b]
Fire pumps	< 200	60
Emergency generators	< 200	60
UPS (uninterruptible power supply) systems	40[c]	30
Control panels for SSIV (sub-sea isolation valve)/SSSV(sub-surface safety valve)/BOP(blowout preventer)	40[c]	15

a In absence of any knowledge regarding the relative location of the fire on the riser, the ESD valves and the contents of the riser, it has been assumed that the fire is near the ESD valves and the riser is filled with liquid hydrocarbon. As a result, 200°C has been used as the default surface temperature for the riser sections to ensure the integrity of the ESD valves.

b Or the minimum time period considered sufficient for a complete evacuation of the installation.

c PFP may be provided to prevent temperature in the enclosure containing this equipment rising to these levels when subjected to an external fire.

Table showing some typical protection period requirements (Based on Table C6 of BS EN ISO 13702:1999, Petroleum and natural gas industries – Control and mitigation of fires and explosions on offshore production installations – Requirements and guidelines)

ACTIVE FIRE PROTECTION

Active fire protection (AFP) is any measure, which, on detection of a fire, is activated to extinguish it or mitigate its effects. Systems can be fixed installations (e.g. sprinkler or deluge systems), or portable (e.g. extinguishers). Commonly, activation of fixed installations is automatic (linked to a detector), with a manual back-up (e.g. opening of a valve or manual activation of a linked alarm call-point).

Water-Based and Foam-Based Fire Protection Systems

A typical **water-based fixed** (i.e. not portable) **installation** comprises:

A FIRE-WATER SOURCE

For example, sea water or a large water storage tank (this may need to be treated against algal growth and filtered to remove debris that might damage the pump).

A FIRE-WATER PUMP

This must deliver to the required pressure and flow rate. Pumps need to activate quickly (and automatically, unless running constantly) and their continued availability must be ensured (e.g. available back-up for when maintenance is undertaken).

FIRE-WATER MAINS

These are pipes transporting the water from the pump to where it is needed – they may be normally dry (i.e. empty) or, for speedier response (but prone to freezing), wet (i.e. continuously charged with water and often kept pressurised with a 'jockey pump'). Sea water is not used to keep wet systems charged because of corrosion and salt blockage of the discharge heads.

DISCHARGE POINT

For example, nozzles, sprinkler heads, monitors, hoses.

Water systems principally work by cooling the fire. Although water-based systems are effective against cellulosic (also called 'Class A') fires, they can be ineffective and actually dangerous if used to try to extinguish hydrocarbon fires (causing it to float and spread). The exception is water mist (see later).

For **fixed-foam systems**, the above installation design (source, pump, etc.) is basically the same, except a foam concentrate is injected into the fire-water system from a separate storage vessel using a metering pump. Foam-based systems are generally very effective for hydrocarbon pool fires, but not for hydrocarbon jet fires. Foam systems work by smothering the fire – creating a layer of foam on the surface which excludes the air; the foam also stops the liquid beneath from forming more vapour.

The common types of water-based and foam-based AFPs are:

SPRINKLER SYSTEMS

Here, the discharge points are high-level mounted sprinkler heads, and each sprinkler head can be activated independently (e.g. by fusable element), discharging onto the area below. These generally use water spray and are used mainly for cellulosic fires, such as may occur in accommodation blocks and general office and storage areas.

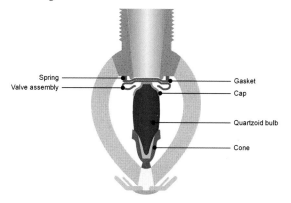

Schematic of a Fixed Installation Water Sprinkler

Fire and Explosion in the Oil and Gas Industries

DELUGE SYSTEMS

This is an AFP system that can use either water or foam as the extinguishant. This is similar to the sprinkler-system arrangement except that it has a single valve controlling flow to multiple high-level, mounted open-discharge heads. Activation of the valve allows water/foam to fall on the fire below from all of the heads at once.

WATER-MIST SYSTEMS

This type of system creates a very fine mist of water droplets and is often used as an alternative to gaseous inerting systems (see below). Research has shown that very fine water mists (less than 400 microns diameter) are effective on both cellulosic type fires (Class A) **and** flammable liquid fires (Class B).

MONITORS

These are like a water cannon, and can be used to direct water jet, water spray, or foam on to a specific area for extinguishment or cooling. Just like a water cannon they can be fixed in position or rotated (horizontally and vertically). They are especially useful where it is not possible to discharge extinguishant from above using deluge systems, e.g. in the case of helidecks and wellheads offshore. Monitors can be permanently installed in position, or portable (with connection to a hydrant).

HOSES

Unless permanently attached hoses are already incorporated into the design, fire-water mains will be equipped with hydrants to facilitate attachment of portable hoses.

DRY CHEMICAL-BASED FIRE PROTECTION SYSTEMS

Here the dry chemical is expelled onto the fire using a pressurised carrier gas. These systems may be incorporated as fixed installations, terminating in either fixed nozzles or hand-held hoses. They can be used on a wide variety of fires, including hydrocarbon jet fires but, as with all dry chemical extinguishants, there is always a danger of re-ignition (it does not cool the fire). They work principally by smothering.

GASEOUS INERTING EXTINGUISHING SYSTEMS

Gases such as carbon dioxide have been widely used in fixed installations to extinguish fires involving live electrical equipment (or at least where electrical disconnection cannot be ensured), such as in machine rooms. Water-based systems are unsuitable in these cases because of the danger of electrocution. These gaseous inerting systems also have the advantage that they cause little mess/damage (unlike water, foam and dry powder). Halons have previously been used but are now banned (except for a few reserved applications) because of their ozone layer damaging potential.

Carbon-dioxide systems work by smothering (i.e. displacing the air/oxygen). There is the clear danger of asphyxiating personnel who happen to be trapped in the area where the system activates. Automatic activation is therefore not desirable without some safeguards, including audible/visual warnings and manual deactivation. Discharge can also generate static electrical discharge.

MOBILE/PORTABLE EQUIPMENT

In addition to the above fixed installations, there is a range of portable equipment, such as extinguishers (water, foam, carbon dioxide, dry powder), portable hoses (for attachment to hydrants) and portable monitors.

AREA/ROOM	TYPE OF PROTECTION IN ADDITION TO PORTABLE	TYPICAL MINIMUM WATER APPLICATION RATES l/MIN/M²	COMMENTS
Wellhead/manifold area	Deluge/foam/dry chemical	10 (or 400 l/min/well)	
Process areas	Deluge/foam/dry chemical	10	
Pumps/compressors	Deluge/foam	20	
Gas treatment area	Deluge/dry chemical	10	Foam, if area contains significant flammable liquids
Methanol area	Alcohol-resistant foam or deluge	10	Portable foam units, if the methanol area is small
Water-injection treatment area	None, if no HC risk		
Drill floor	Deluge	10	Only if FES (Fire and Emergency Strategy) shows role for this system
BOP (blowout preventer) area	Deluge/foam	400	
Drillers cabin	None		
Degasser room	Deluge/foam	10	Only if FES shows role for this system
Shale shaker room	Deluge/foam	10	
Active mud-tank room	Deluge/foam	10	
Sack/bulk storage room	None		Provided that no flammable materials stored
Mud lab	None		
Cementing unit room	Water-mist/deluge/foam		Water-mist according to supplier requirement
Control station (CS)	None		To be confirmed in developing FES
Central control room (CCR)	None		To be confirmed in developing FES
Instrument room adjacent to CS/CCR	None		To be confirmed in developing FES
Local equipment room	None		To be confirmed in developing FES
False floor and ceiling in CS/CCR and instrument rooms			Lifting gear for floor hatches. Gaseous system with lance.
Turbine hall	Deluge	10	Dedicated system only if flammable inventories within the hall
Turbine hood	CO_2 gaseous or water-mist		Interlock access to hood, if gaseous
Switch-board room	None		To be confirmed in developing FES

Table showing selection of AFP systems (Based on Table C3 of BS EN ISO 13702:1999, Petroleum and natural gas industries – Control and mitigation of fires and explosions on offshore production installations – Requirements and guidelines)

Fire and Explosion in the Oil and Gas Industries

SPECIFIC EXAMPLES OF FIRE PROTECTION SYSTEMS

The following fire protection measures would be used in addition to design features such as bunding, pressure relief, overfilling level alarms, siting (i.e. separation/spacing), emergency shut-off devices and control of ignition sources.

You will probably remember most of the following terms from earlier in the course.

FIXED-ROOF TANKS

Typical protection would include foam injection in the event of a fire. This is either overhead (where injectors are sited inside the vessel just below the line of the roof) or sub-surface (foam is injected from beneath the liquid surface, the foam rising and covering the surface). Remotely activated foam monitors can provide further protection, by directing a jet of foam onto the roof of the vessel. Water-deluge cooling sprays might also be used.

FLOATING-ROOF TANKS

The main means of fire protection is to use fixed foam installations, which spread foam around the rim seal. As for fixed-roof tanks, monitors and water-deluge cooling sprays may also be used.

PROCESS MODULES

Fires and explosions have happened as a result of gas leaks and liquid spills (e.g. the Piper Bravo gas explosion in 1994 – this rig replaced Piper Alpha, destroyed in 1988). Measures include gas leak-detection equipment, overhead foam deluge, foam monitors and hydrants/hoses.

GLOSSARY

FIXED-ROOF TANKS
Used to store liquids like petroleum and crude oil in bulk at or near atmospheric pressure; they are vertical cylindrical storage tanks.

FLOATING-ROOF TANKS
A variant of the above but the tank roof is floating directly on the surface of the liquid within (i.e. not fixed, it moves up and down with the level of the liquid); there is a flexible seal between the rim of the roof and the tank wall.

PROCESS MODULES
An oil rig/platform is modular; the process module is a confined area where gas and water are separated from the oil. The water is usually treated before being emptied into the sea. The gas is used for gas compression/reinjection into wells and any excess gas is burnt off at the flare stack.

SPHERES
Spherical-shaped storage vessels, which may be used for storing, among other things, liquefied natural gas (LNG) and liquefied petroleum gas (LPG).

SPHERES

Situating the vessel underground is, in itself, an effective fire protection strategy but does cause problems for maintenance and leak detection. Spheres are fitted with gas-leak detectors, where possible. Above-ground vessels (and supports and associated equipment) may be treated with passive fire protection, such as spray-applied coatings (including cement-based and intumescent types), or mineral fibres. Water-deluge systems and monitors can be used for vessel cooling.

GAS TURBINES AND COMPRESSORS

Gas turbines and gas compressor units are enclosed in fire-resisting enclosures (i.e. using fire barriers). Leakage of gas could lead to explosion and fire, so it is usual to monitor the atmosphere using gas detectors. Extinguishment within such enclosures is achieved with fixed installations using carbon dioxide or water mist.

REFINERY PROCESS UNITS AND STORAGE TERMINALS

Active fire protection systems such as water-sprinkler and spray systems are widely used in refineries for protection of process plant, storage vessels and loading facilities. They are designed to extinguish the fire, control the fire, or protect adjacent plant from exposure in a fire situation. Foam pourers or fixed water jets may be used in addition to sprays or sprinklers and also specialised systems using inert gases for flooding enclosed spaces. Water jets and sprays are also employed to cool adjacent process equipment not directly involved in the fire.

Passive fire protection such as fire-resistant insulating coatings may be used to protect against vessel failure where water or other active protection media supplies are inadequate, such as in remote locations, or where there are difficulties with handling fire-water run-off. Fire walls are another form of passive fire protection that are used to prevent fire spread and exposure of adjacent plant to thermal radiation.

REVISION QUESTIONS

1. In relation to fire protection, outline the principle of operation of a voting system and when it might be used.

2. Outline the main components of a fixed water-deluge system.

3. Describe the difference between active and passive fire protection measures.

4. Outline the fire protection that would be used on a floating roof tank.

(Suggested Answers are at the end.)

Emergency Response

Emergencies can and do happen. Emergency response preparedness is essential; it saves lives and minimises damage to property and the environment by bringing things under control quickly. A strategy to prevent major accidents can be conveniently broken down into three parts:

- **Identification of an installation as a major hazard installation** – this usually entails notification to the authorities, based on regulatory criteria (type of activity and/or inventory of hazardous substances).
- **Prevention and control** – after assessing the likely risks, putting in place effective measures to control them.
- **Mitigation** – which is where emergency planning comes in, to help minimise the effects of major accidents that do occur, despite the controls.

EMERGENCY RESPONSE PLAN (ERP)

Role and Importance

You will remember from Element 1 the need for emergency plans as part of safety cases.

A written ERP communicates to all parties what action to take, who will take it and the resources needed for all likely emergencies and subsequent clean-up operations. It means that emergencies have been thought through before they happen, so that when they do occur you will understand far better what is going on and what to do. Prompt action in an emergency makes all the difference between an incident and a catastrophe.

A written ERP also provides documentary evidence of preparedness to regulators (especially in the case of an investigation).

In the UK, it is a legal requirement for operators of high-hazard installations to prepare ERPs, e.g.

- For onshore activities, under the **Control of Major Accident Hazards (COMAH) Regulations 1999**.
- For offshore activities, under the **Offshore Installations (Safety Case) Regulations 2005** and the **Prevention of Fire and Explosion and Emergency Response (PFEER) on Offshore Installations Regulations 1995**.

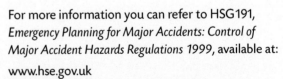

MORE...

For more information you can refer to HSG191, *Emergency Planning for Major Accidents: Control of Major Accident Hazards Regulations 1999*, available at: www.hse.gov.uk

BS EN ISO 15544:2010 offers specific advice for offshore emergency response.

Content of ERPs

The ERP needs to be specific to the installation, covering operational and procedural needs for each emergency situation. The detail will therefore vary but it will generally consider such things as:

- Specific foreseeable emergency situations (or types) and their likely scale and consequences.

  Some emergencies may be similar and treated together. Some of these will be relatively minor and can be dealt with by on-site crew but others will be major (e.g. requiring abandonment of an offshore rig and/or external help). Some will be natural (e.g. severe storms) and some will arise entirely from the hazardous activities being carried out.

- Organisational roles, authority, responsibilities and expertise.

  For example, emergency response team, incident command structure, etc.

- Emergency response actions/procedures.

  These need to consider each situation from detection and raising the alarm, to the point at which the emergency has been controlled (if this is possible) and all personnel are in a 'place of safety'. Procedures may be required for emergency shutdown, clean-up, decontamination and process re-start.

- Sufficient resources.

  People (shift-work coverage, equipment, materials), including any specialised emergency response equipment needed, e.g. in an emergency control centre.

- Evacuation procedures.

- Communications.

  Including between emergency responders (e.g. by radio), internal and external (regulatory) incident-reporting, calling external help (escalation) and dealing with the media.

- Training for personnel and drills to test the plan.

  We will discuss some of these issues in more detail later.

Because the incident may well require the intervention of external resources, emergency services and regulatory agencies (either to assist with on-site mitigation, or if the incident extends off-site) should be consulted on the development of the emergency plan for the site/installation. In the UK, there is a statutory duty to consult in such cases. If installations are connected (e.g. by pipeline, as in the case of some offshore rigs such as Piper Alpha) these installations should consult with each other and co-ordinate their response plans. Since the Piper Alpha incident, additional safety precautions have been required, e.g. Emergency Shutdown (ESD) valves fitted to a platform receiving oil/gas from another platform.

Fire and Explosion Strategy (FES)

A **fire and explosion strategy** (FES) is the output of a process which evaluates fire and explosion scenarios and the mitigation measures needed. In other words, it is a record of a specific fire and explosion risk assessment and may simply be an integral part of a wider risk assessment for the entire installation, rather than a separate document. As with all risk assessments, complex cases will require more detail (e.g. computer-based dispersion modelling) whereas simple cases are more likely to rely on industry-standard codes of practice. Evaluations would typically consider:

- The foreseeable fires/explosions (cellulosic, hydrocarbon pool, hydrocarbon jet).
- Their likelihood of occurrence and likely severity, which may depend on:
  - Location (accommodation, process module, helideck, etc.).
  - Nature of the gas/liquid, the way in which they are being handled (temperature/pressure) and the amounts in use.
  - Complexity of the installation.
- Other related issues, such as:
  - Human factors (i.e. how people behave in a fire/explosion).
  - Remoteness of the installation (proximity of external help).

This evaluation will allow selection of the most appropriate fire/explosion prevention and mitigation measures, depending on the risk. This will then feed into the operational and procedural requirements in the ERP.

ALARMS

Alarms may be automatically or manually activated. Manual alarms (call points) often supplement automatic systems. Alarms may be incorporated into fixed fire-water installations (when they are driven by the water flow and referred to as 'gongs'). Fire and gas-detection systems will typically also initiate an alarm and some control action (such as emergency shut-down, or activation of fire suppression). Alarms give an audible or visual warning to personnel and, because there can be several different types of emergencies, may be varied to indicate different responses by personnel.

Emergency Response

For example, BS EN ISO 13702:1999 suggests the following standard for offshore installations:

ALARM TYPE	PRIMARY	SUPPLEMENTARY
Muster	Intermittent signal of constant frequency	Flashing yellow
Prepare to abandon	Continuous signal of variable frequency	Flashing yellow
Toxic	Continuous signal of constant frequency	Flashing red in affected area

Table showing primary is audible, supplementary (for very noisy areas) is visual. (Based on Table B1 of BS EN ISO 13702:1999, Petroleum and natural gas industries – Control and mitigation of fires and explosions on offshore production installations – Requirements and guidelines)

Offshore installations also commonly have **status lights**:

- Green – normal.
- Yellow – indicates low-level alert – gas.
- Red – indicates high-level alert – gas.
- Blue – indicates abandon platform.

MEDICAL EMERGENCY PLANNING

Medical emergencies will require prompt treatment. In planning, you will need to consider matters such as:

RANGE OF LIKELY MEDICAL EMERGENCIES.

For example, severe injuries from major accidents, heart attacks and, for offshore, problems such as food poisoning and epidemics (which may seriously compromise the safe running of the installation). There will also be the common minor injuries.

PERSONNEL (TRAINED AND ADEQUATE NUMBER) AND EQUIPMENT NEEDED FOR TREATMENT AND EVACUATION.

The remoteness of the site and harshness of the environment have a large influence here; having on-site capability is especially important for remote sites in hostile environments like offshore oil platforms, which must consider a wider range of potential emergencies because external help would never arrive in time.

Level 3 personnel (medics, paramedics and similar technicians) will have specific medical training and be capable of administering drugs, advanced wound treatment, etc.

Some offshore installations have extensive facilities (including equipment such as X-ray machines), staffed by nurses and medics.

NEED TO TRANSPORT/EVACUATE THE SICK/INJURED TO OFF-SITE MEDICAL FACILITIES.

The response needs to be proportionate. On-site emergency health care usually adopts a tiered approach:

- Level 1 - Basic first-aid.
- Level 2 - Advanced first-aid.

- Level 3 – Using medics or paramedics with remote support from other medical professionals.

First-aid (Level 1 and 2) is first-line treatment to preserve life and stabilise the injured. This will require the provision of:

AN ADEQUATE NUMBER OF TRAINED FIRST-AIDERS.

The number and level of training required for first-aiders depends on the level of risk from the activities, the number of workers, installation remoteness, etc. Onshore installations close to hospitals will probably not have the same requirements as an offshore installation. In the former case, fewer first-aiders (with basic training only) may be adequate, whereas offshore first-aiders may require more advanced training on specific techniques, e.g. management of bleeding, use of specialist equipment.

FIRST-AID EQUIPMENT.

Such as first-aid kit supplies, any specialist treatments, recovery room, automatic external defibrillators (AEDs), etc.

> MORE...
>
> OGP Report: *Managing health for field operations in oil and gas activities*. Report No. 343
> www.ogp.org.uk/pubs/343.pdf

Medical Evacuation and Back-Up

A medical emergency may require evacuation of the injured to a secondary health-care facility (i.e. off-site hospital) or tertiary health-care facility (i.e. specialist hospital unit, such as for cardiac patients or severe burns). Procedures for evacuation need to be developed and would consider:

HEALTH RISK TO THE PATIENT

Both the urgency of the transfer and the extra risks posed by the transport itself, e.g. emergency air transport is not recommended for certain medical conditions. This will obviously require a medical assessment.

SCALE OF THE EMERGENCY

Single versus multiple casualties.

RESOURCES REQUIRED AND AVAILABLE

Vehicle and accompanying trained personnel, including escorts such as first-aiders. This may be contracted out.

Evacuation may be by land (such as by ambulance), sea or air (e.g. helicopter air ambulance) and, in each case, the vehicle/vessel/craft needs to be capable of accommodating and securing the patient and must be fitted with medical equipment/staff needed to stabilise the patient during the journey.

PRINCIPLES OF ESCAPE, EVACUATION AND RESCUE

In an emergency, time is of the essence. Escape routes should therefore be designed to allow people to escape to a place of safety as quickly as possible. Thus, escape routes must be:

WIDE ENOUGH.

Take account of the injured, stretchers, equipment and numbers of personnel – at least 1 metre wide.

SUFFICIENT IN NUMBER FOR THE NUMBER OF PERSONNEL AND FORESEEN EMERGENCY SCENARIOS.

An important principle here is that of redundancy, i.e. there should be enough capacity/alternative routes in case one route is blocked by fire/smoke. Offshore accommodation modules should have at least two separate means of escape (as far apart as possible – at least 45° – so that it is unlikely both will be blocked by fire/smoke). These should lead directly to a relatively safe place (muster point, evacuation point, sea escape point, etc).

PROTECTED AGAINST THE EFFECTS OF FIRE/EXPLOSION.

This can be achieved by virtue of position (i.e. separate and sited away from blast panels, etc.) and/or by special fire protection (e.g. fire barriers). However, emergency-escape breathing apparatus may also be needed to ensure this.

Lifts should not be used in emergency evacuation (unless they are specially designed for this purpose).

CLEARLY DESIGNATED AND ILLUMINATED.

Emergency exit signage and other markings, which can be seen under fire/smoke conditions, e.g. wayfinder lights to lifeboat stations.

Typical Fire-Exit Sign

MAINTAINED CLEAR OF OBSTRUCTIONS.

Doors should open outwards (i.e. in the direction of travel), where possible.

Escape in an emergency requires safe routes from where people are working to get to designated muster points or **temporary refuges**. Temporary refuges are places that are relatively safe. They can be in the form of a fire-protected enclosure, or simply an open area, sufficiently far away from the incident. They need to be large enough to accommodate personnel who have been instructed to go there.

The **muster point** itself must be relatively safe and, in the first instance, would most likely be on-site. If the emergency is sufficiently serious, personnel will then need to be evacuated from muster points to a place of safety off-site. Off-site evacuation obviously presents more difficulties for offshore installations.

Evacuation Off Site

For onshore facilities, evacuation off site is easily achieved by walking or land-based transport. Offshore evacuation options are:

PRIMARY METHOD

This would preferably use the normal non-emergency method, e.g. by ship, if transport is normally by ship to the installation.

SECONDARY METHOD

The primary method may not always be available, so a back-up method is needed, e.g. survival craft (i.e. a lifeboat), situated close to the temporary refuge and launched from the installation. It is normal to allow a safety factor of at least 50% spare survival craft capacity. In all departments, there should be trained coxswains on shifts who are lifeboat captains.

TERTIARY METHODS

These are the final options and will include personal equipment such as lifejackets, liferafts and survival suits. These are not without risk (jumping into the sea from high up can cause injury or death). Personnel will need to be recovered from the sea and may have very limited survival time in hostile sea/weather conditions (hypothermia and exhaustion).

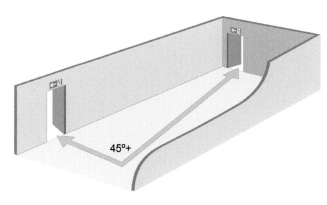

45°+

Alternative Exit Routes

Emergency Response

Recovery and Rescue

Recovery from the sea will be required when, for example:

- A tertiary evacuation method has been used.
- A helicopter has had to ditch into the sea.
- Someone has fallen into the sea from the installation.
- Certain secondary evacuation methods have been used, e.g. survival craft are not designed to transport personnel to a place of ultimate safety, so require further intervention.

Recovery might be achieved using a dedicated rescue and recovery ship, stationed in the vicinity.

As distinct from 'recovery', someone is not considered 'rescued' until they have been recovered to a place where they can receive medical attention.

ROLES AND OPERATION OF FIRE TEAMS

Members of the fire team have specific responsibilities to fight fire in an emergency. They are also referred to as the emergency response team (ERT), especially if they have a role in wider emergencies. A large site may have a dedicated fire brigade that will perform this function. The exact nature of the responsibilities will depend on each installation and there is a clear need for remote/offshore installations to be more self-reliant because of the considerable delay in external emergency services reaching them.

To handle incidents, major-hazard installations have tended to adopt the responsibilities and command structure typically used by emergency services, like the fire brigade.

Onshore Installations

For onshore installations, the structure typically consists of the following roles, but it is important that the command structure is as similar as possible to normal command hierarchy and as simple as possible, to avoid role confusion during an incident:

INCIDENT CONTROLLER (IC)

This person takes on-site control of the incident. Because of the wide-ranging site knowledge needed, this role is usually held by a site manager or very experienced supervisor, with cover constantly maintained. The IC will be set up close to the incident and will:

- Determine if an incident of which they have been notified is serious (or likely to be) and, if so, initiate the emergency plan.
- Assume some **Main Controller** (MC) responsibilities, if they are absent, to ensure:
  - External emergency services are alerted (as necessary).
  - Alarms have been activated and warnings given (the public may need alerting).
  - Plant shut down (if necessary) and evacuation.
  - Key personnel are summoned (such as members of the emergency response team).

- Co-ordinate incident response activities (i.e. search and rescue, fire-fighting – though emergency services would take control upon arrival on site, aided by the site's emergency response/fire team).
- Establish and maintain communications (e.g. on-going radio communication situation reports to the main controller in the **Emergency Control Centre** (ECC), providing information to emergency services).

MAIN CONTROLLER (MC)

The Main Controller has overall responsibility and will usually be stationed in an emergency control centre in a safe location. Again, the role requires someone with good knowledge of the site/installation and seniority, such as a site manager or offshore installation manager (with contingency back-up). The IC will assume some of the MC responsibilities until they arrive. In addition to the above specific MC responsibilities, he/she has other important responsibilities, including:

- Keeping the incident under review as it develops – trying to predict which way it is likely to go, given the current information.
- Making sure casualties are being treated.
- Liaising with external agencies/sources, e.g. coastguard, air/sea rescue, fire brigade, police, ambulance, regulatory authority, weather information services, etc. – this is especially important if the situation is likely to have off-site effects, such as a cloud of toxic smoke drifting towards a residential area.
- Controlling traffic.
- Keeping a record of the development of events and decisions made and, as far as possible, preserving evidence ('learning from incidents' and may also be required for possible legal case).
- Welfare needs – if the incident is protracted, food/drink may need to be arranged.
- Dealing with the media.
- Recovery and clean-up of the area/plant afterwards.

> ### GLOSSARY
>
> **EMERGENCY CONTROL CENTRE (ECC)**
> An on-site area or building that is in a safe place and is the hub of the emergency response operations, run by the Main Controller. It is fitted out with communications equipment (radios, telephones), site plans, site information, etc.

EMERGENCY RESPONSE/FIRE-TEAM MEMBERS

While the IC and MC are technically part of the team, these are the people who will actually be doing the tasks, such as fighting fires, search and rescue, administering first aid, etc. rather than directing operations. Obviously, they need to be competent and fit to perform their assigned duties.

Offshore Installations

For offshore installations, the terminology and command structure is different. In such circumstances, the **Offshore Installation Manager** (OIM) is in overall charge. He/she will be assisted by two on-scene commanders (one from drilling and one from process), a permit controller, a radio operator and an Offshore Installation Supervisor (OIS). They have direct contact with onshore and the coastguard. Especially important offshore services responsibilities are:

- Monitoring the weather conditions (wind speed and direction, etc.).
- The positioning of the standby boat.
- Communications with the fire teams.

TRAINING AND DRILLS

So that each person knows what to do in an emergency, they need training commensurate with their role. All site personnel (including contractors) will at the very least receive basic instruction on induction, e.g.

- Raising the alarm.
- Evacuation routes.
- Where to muster.
- Depending on the site: use of any emergency life-saving equipment (emergency BA, survival suits, etc.) and basic first aid.

Those with specific responsibilities need additional training in topics related to their duties, such as:

- **Fire-team members**: fire behaviour, fire-fighting techniques, fire extinguishment, use of breathing apparatus, search and rescue, communications equipment, etc.

- **MCs, ICs, OIMs, and OISs**: analysing incidents and decision-making during incidents, adequate evidence recording, etc. OIMs and OISs also routinely undergo specialist fire-team training.
- **Control-room operators**: how to deal with operational emergencies, including radio operation during emergencies (mayday distress calls).
- **Helideck crew**: specialist helideck emergency training.

Refresher training is needed to maintain competence, but that is not enough on its own. Drills (i.e. simulations of real emergency events) also play an important role; they check that people will respond as intended in emergencies.

Drills should be organised throughout the year, covering a range of possible incidents and conditions. There are different types of drills, ranging from 'table-top' theoretical exercises (which help practise and verify problem-solving skills) to a full-scale 'realistic' exercise, involving all personnel and possibly also off-site emergency services. It is also possible to test specific parts of the emergency response system or the whole system. Drills are carried out every seven days; usually, a more elaborate exercise is conducted every two to three months.

LIAISON WITH EXTERNAL SUPPORT AGENCIES AND RESOURCES AND EMERGENCY SERVICES

External agencies that may be needed include: fire brigade, ambulance, coast guard, police, air ambulance, local municipal authority, health authority, environmental regulator (e.g. Environment Agency), safety regulator (e.g. HSE). Support may also be needed from utility (electricity, water, gas, telephone) providers. Some resources, such as support vessels or air ambulances, may also be pooled/shared between sites/installations or operators or even provided by a separate company under contract.

GLOSSARY

UPSTREAM OIL AND GAS INDUSTRY
Those activities associated with exploration, extraction and production of crude oil and gas.

DOWNSTREAM OIL AND GAS INDUSTRY
Activities associated with refining, storage, distribution and sale of oil and gas products, e.g. petrol.

REVISION QUESTIONS

5. Outline what is meant by a 'Fire and Explosion Strategy'.

6. Outline the tiered, three-level approach to emergency medical treatment.

7. Distinguish between primary, secondary and tertiary offshore evacuation methods.

8. What is the difference between 'recovery' and 'rescue'?

9. Give a brief summary of the emergency command structure for offshore installations.

(Suggested Answers are at the end.)

SUMMARY

This element has considered fire and evacuation issues in the oil and gas industry. In particular, it has:

- Discussed the detection of leaks of gas, vapours, liquids and oil mists, noting the importance of location, maintenance and integrity.
- Considered fire detection systems, looking at those designed to monitor for smoke (ionisation, scattering), heat (fixed-temperature and rate-of-rise types) and flame (UV, visible, IR).
- Explained passive fire protection, designed to insulate structures and components from excessive heat, and noted the various forms in which this comes, such as: spray-applied coatings, jackets, sealants, pre-formed sections.
- Discussed active fire protection, designed to tackle the fire, looking at fixed installations (water/foam deluge, sprinklers, gas inerting) and portable equipment (such as extinguishers, portable hoses and monitors).
- Given typical examples of fire protection as applied to tanks, spheres, etc.
- Highlighted the significance of emergency planning considerations such as risk assessment, foreseeable emergencies, establishing a command structure, etc.
- Explained the importance of medical provision in case of emergency, looking at the different levels of such provision (ranging from basic first aid to trained medics).
- Considered emergency evacuation, especially the need to establish and maintain evacuation routes and provide for evacuation to a safe place away from the installation.
- Discussed the need for training to maintain readiness of the response team and other workers, and the importance of liaising with external agencies such as hospitals, the coastguard and regulators.

Exam Skills

QUESTION

A floating-roof tank used for storing petroleum products currently has no fire protection in place. CCTV cameras are the only form of leak detection currently used on the site. You have been tasked with selecting additional leak detectors and fire protection equipment.

(a) Outline the issues/factors to take into account in selecting this additional leak-detection equipment. (4)

(b) Give the meaning of the term 'active fire protection'. (2)

(c) Identify TWO suitable forms of active fire protection that could be used for this type of tank. (2)

APPROACHING THE QUESTION

- Using the system we have covered, the first thing to do is read the question carefully. There are three parts to this question. You are asked to outline issues from selecting leak-detection equipment, give a meaning and identify two forms of active fire protection. You should structure your approach (a bullet-point list can be used to identify the issues) and expand into outlines afterwards.

- Next, consider the marks available. In this question there are eight marks; we can see that the question awards four marks for (a), and two marks each for (b) and (c).

- The question should take around eight minutes.

- Now highlight the key words. In this case, it might look like this:

  a) Outline the issues/factors to take into account in selecting this additional leak-detection equipment. (4)

  b) Give the meaning of the term 'active fire protection'. (2)

  c) Identify TWO suitable forms of active fire protection that could be used for this type of tank. (2)

- Read the question again – make sure you understand it.

- Following this, the next stage is to develop a plan. Remember, a plan can be completed in various ways, but it could consist of the following:

SUGGESTED ANSWER

Plan

The question requires	Answers include
Issues to take into account **selecting** leak detectors	Location (properties of gas). High level not best if gas is dense. Would locating inside bund be better? What are local air flows like? How many detectors? Maintenance and testing of detectors. Uninterruptible power supply. Suitability for environment. Reliability.
What is 'active fire protection'?	Extinguishers. Sprinklers. Deluge systems. All actively PUT OUT fires.
Types of active fire protection	Fixed deluge system. Foam monitors. Water deluge.

Now have a go at the question yourself.

Exam skills

POSSIBLE ANSWER BY EXAM CANDIDATE

(a) The issues to take into account include:

- The location of the detectors – taking into account the properties of the gas, such as its density and tendency to collect in low-lying areas. Because of this, placing them at high level may not be advisable; putting them in the bund at low level might be better.
- What are local air flows like – what dispersal or dilution properties will they have?
- How many detectors will be required, based on the number of likely leak locations, such as valves, joints, seams, etc?
- We must provide adequate maintenance and testing of the detectors and put in place maintenance and testing plans and records.
- Detectors will need an uninterruptible electrical power supply in case of power failure on the installation, and they must be robust enough to endure the rigours of the environment and be intrinsically safe. The detectors must be reliable.

(b) 'Active fire protection' means the provision of equipment, systems and methods, which, following initiation, may be used to control, mitigate and extinguish fires.

(c) Rim fires are the most likely to occur with floating-roof tanks, so suitable forms of active fire protection would include:

- A fixed foam-deluge system at high level, supplemented with foam monitors on the ground.
- A water-deluge system for cooling the outer shell of the tank.

REASONS FOR POOR MARKS ACHIEVED BY CANDIDATES IN EXAM

- Not answering the question at all. If you do not attempt all questions required you cannot get any marks.
- Not following a structured approach: remember, the question is in three parts. The question asked you to **outline**, **give** and **identify**, so lists for parts (a) and (c) would not gain maximum marks.
- Not balancing the answers – part (a) will need more information to be given than the other two parts.
- Giving lots of other information not relevant to the question.

LOGISTICS AND TRANSPORT OPERATIONS

ELEMENT
5

LEARNING OUTCOMES

On completion of this element, you should be able to demonstrate understanding of the content by applying what you have learnt to familiar and unfamiliar situations. In particular, you should be able to:

❶ Identify the main hazards of and suitable controls for marine transport in the oil and gas industries.

❷ Identify the main hazards of and suitable controls for land transport in the oil and gas industries.

Contents

Marine Transport

HAZARDS OF VESSELS AND WORKING OVER WATER

The offshore oil industry uses a vast array of marine vessels and structures, ranging from the large (floating oil rigs and oil tankers) to the small (survival craft).

The floating production, storage and offloading (**FPSO**) vessel performs the key functions of:

- Receiving hydrocarbons produced from nearby platforms.
- Processing them.
- Storing them.
- Off-loading them via a tanker or a pipeline.

FPSOs are often converted oil tankers, or may be vessels built specially for the application.

Other vessels may perform a more limited range of functions such as:

- Floating storage and offloading unit (**FSO**) – used only to store oil and off-load to oil tankers.
- Floating storage unit (**FSU**) – used to transfer oil by pipeline to a land-based facility.

Similar vessels (**FSRUs** – floating storage and regasification units) are used to store and handle liquefied natural gas (**LNG**). They receive LNG from other vessels, convert the liquid back into gas and distribute it via pipelines to onshore facilities.

Marine Transport

As well as the intrinsic dangers associated with planned operations on board and beneath such vessels, there are the specific issues of:

- Extreme environmental conditions (weather, waves, sea currents/temperature, ice, etc).
- Accelerated wear and corrosion – the stress of constant movement/buffeting and aggressive salt spray means that structures and equipment can quickly fail if maintenance is neglected. We looked at this in an earlier element.
- Collisions with other vessels and structures (including running aground and damage from icebergs) – these may also result in environmental damage (oil spills). An inadequate/defective mooring, combined with extreme weather may contribute to this. We will look at control of vessel design and marine operations later.
- The intrinsic hazards of the substances – we looked at the hazards of the main substances in Element 1, e.g. LNG, hydrogen sulphide and drilling fluids ('mud'). We also looked at the potential for fire and the different methods of fire and explosion protection in earlier elements.
- Oil/LNG transfer operations – which, again, could result in environmental damage (oil spills). We will look at loading/unloading operations later.
- Personnel transfer operations – see later in this element.
- Drilling-rig hazards (other than those already mentioned, such as fire and substances in use) – working at height, manual handling.
- Lone working (we will look at diving operations later).
- Personnel falling overboard (through tripping, slipping), with the risk of cold shock (from icy water), extreme fatigue (the effort to stay afloat with water-logged clothing), hypothermia (if not rescued immediately) and drowning. We looked at recovery and rescue in the last element.
- Piracy (a specific problem around East Africa/Somalia). We will look at some aspects of vessel safety/security later.

MORE...

Guidelines for Managing Marine Risks Associated with FPSOs (OGP (International Association of Oil & Gas Producers) Report No. 377)

LOADING AND UNLOADING OF VESSELS AT MARINE TERMINALS

A marine oil and gas terminal is a dock where ships/tankers moor to transfer crude oil (and derived products) and gas (LNG, LPG) to, or from, storage facilities. Some terminals are onshore and some are offshore. You will notice that F(P)SO/FSU can be regarded as off-shore terminals in this respect, though transfer will only be from the storage unit to the ship/tanker. Activities at terminals would include escorting (by use of tug boat) to safely berth/moor the ship and offloading/loading (using hoses, pipelines or loading arms). Some tankers ('supertankers') may be too large to moor at the terminal itself. In these cases, ship-to-ship transfers are the usual solution, whereby liquid from the larger ship is transferred by hose to a smaller, lighter vessel, which can then moor at the terminal. This process is called 'lightering'.

MORE...

International Safety Guide for Oil Tankers and Terminals (ISGOTT)

In general:

- The ship should be securely moored.
- The responsible people in charge of the terminal and the tanker, respectively, should agree a loading/off-loading plan (exchanging information about the cargo, transfer rates, venting, quantities, communications/signals, etc). A checklist is used for this purpose. For tanker loading operations, this may involve the inspection of tanks and verification of the previous load and tank cleanliness.
- Ship doors, ports, windows, etc. that open onto the tank deck should be kept closed (to avoid ingress of flammable vapours, and the risk of explosion in accommodation areas). Ventilation systems may also have to be adjusted or disconnected so that they do not suck in flammable vapours, or act as an ignition source. Cargo-tank vents should be protected by flame arresters.
- Ship-to-terminal connections (such as via directly connecting hose or marine loading arms (also known as metal cargo arms)) can be fitted with an emergency release.
- Liquid loading lines and vapour emission-control lines (vapour recovery) should be clearly distinguished, to avoid misconnection (this would typically be by unique connection design, so that they cannot be inadvertently connected to the wrong line).
- Hoses should be inspected for defects before use (they should be subject to periodic pressure testing). Hoses located under water will require periodic inspection by divers.

TOPIC FOCUS

Ship-to-Terminal Electric Currents, Earthing and Bonding

Ships are not generally earth-bonded to onshore terminals during off-loading/loading operations. This sounds counter to what you may have heard. This is because the electrical current flow from ship to marine terminal is largely not electrostatic in origin; rather, it arises from galvanic potential differences between them as well as installed cathodic protection devices (to protect against corrosion). A shore-side marine loading arm (all-metal construction) obviously conducts electricity well and is very likely to cause a discharge spark on connection to/disconnection from the ship.

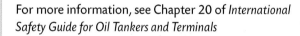

MORE...

For more information, see Chapter 20 of *International Safety Guide for Oil Tankers and Terminals*

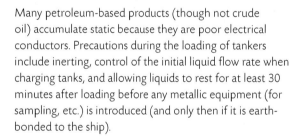

- The position of the hoses/loading arms should be adjusted (or take account of the rising and falling of the ship) so as not to place undue strain on the components (the hoses themselves, ship's manifold connection, etc.). Wind-loading can be a particular issue for marine loading arms, and can place additional strain on connections.
- The weather should be monitored before and during the operation, with the operation being suspended in cases where high winds or electrical storms are expected.
- Crews should keep watch for leaks during the operation, and be prepared to stop if leaks are detected.
- Precautions against electrical discharge need to be observed. For electrical discharge between ship and terminal, this is most likely to arise during terminal hose/arm connection to the ship manifold, so the connection to the ship either uses an insulating (i.e. non-conductive) flange, or a length of insulating hose – the ship-side and terminal-side are then electrically isolated from each other. It has been found that the previous practice of earth-bonding the ship to the terminal is ineffective (and, in fact, dangerous in some cases) and so is not generally recommended (see Topic Focus). In addition, precautions against static electrical discharge (ship–side or terminal-side) should be observed.

Many petroleum-based products (though not crude oil) accumulate static because they are poor electrical conductors. Precautions during the loading of tankers include inerting, control of the initial liquid flow rate when charging tanks, and allowing liquids to rest for at least 30 minutes after loading before any metallic equipment (for sampling, etc.) is introduced (and only then if it is earth-bonded to the ship).

- Co-ordinate activities (or take precautions), e.g. if hazardous activities are being undertaken in adjacent tanker berths. Do not allow tugs, helicopters, etc. to approach too close during the operation (or suspend operations if they must).

There should be joint formal agreement between the master of the vessel and the terminal authority on readiness to load/unload cargo. No transfer should take place before this. Both sides should monitor the operation and communicate throughout.

Marine Transport

Appendix 2 of *Guidelines for Managing Marine Risks Associated with FPSOs* (OGP (International Association of Oil & Gas Producers) Report No. 377) includes a checklist of hazards associated with floating production, storage and offloading units (FPSOs), which includes:

- Leaks of gas and/or oil arising from:
    - Blowouts.
    - Pipeline leaks.
    - Process leaks.
- Non-process incidents such as:
    - Fires.
    - Chemical spills and leaks.
- Marine events such as:
    - Collisions of supply, stand-by and support vessels.
    - Collisions with other vessels.
    - Capsize or grounding.
- Extreme loadings due to wind or waves.
- Structural failure due to:
    - Fatigue.
    - Design error.
- Failure of derricks, cranes or other equipment.
- Dropped objects during:
    - Construction.
    - Crane operations.
    - Cargo transfer.
    - Drilling operations.
- Transport activities (crew changes/in-field transfers):
    - Helicopter crash or fire during refuelling.
    - Capsize of crew boats or accident to personnel during transfer.
- Construction accidents:
    - Onshore or offshore work.
    - Marine installation.
    - Commissioning activities.
    - Pipe laying.
- Diving accidents.
- Slips, trips.

CONTROL OF MARINE OPERATIONS, CERTIFICATION OF VESSELS, INSPECTION AND APPROVALS

You will already be familiar with one form of control of oil and gas marine/offshore installations – the safety case regime. This runs in parallel with other regulatory controls on vessels.

All vessels undergoing international voyages (like tankers) are subject to a system known as **flagging**, i.e. it must be registered to a country and abide by its maritime regulations. As an example, a UK-registered vessel ("UK Flagged") must comply with the requirements of the UK's Maritime and Coastguard Agency (MCA). These requirements derive from those of the International Maritime Organisation (IMO).

Typically, this would mean:

CERTIFICATION/APPROVAL

Depending on the vessel it would need certificates of:

- Safety construction (i.e. it is safely designed and constructed).
- Oil-pollution prevention (i.e. that it complies with the MARPOL (marine pollution) convention requirements).
- Loadline (to help guard against overloading and the vessel sitting too low in the water).
- Tonnage (ships must pay a tax on entering ports and this is levied based on their tonnage).
- Mobile offshore drilling unit (MODU) safety (i.e. compliance with the IMO requirements for the safety of MODUs).
- Shipboard safety management (i.e. the ship operates to a documented, effective safety management system).
- Class (i.e. it conforms to established rules on design, build, inspection and maintenance for that class of vessel) – these certificates would normally be issued by independent verifiers called 'Classification Societies'.

The operator would also need certificates for certain on-board equipment such as cranes (and other lifting equipment) and, of course, the master and crew must be certified as competent (e.g. qualifications such as a master marine certificate) and fit. Some state flag regimes will have specific additional requirements and there are the usual insurance certification requirements.

INSPECTION

To maintain Class certification, ships must undergo periodic inspection by the classification society. This would mean routine annual surveys together with a five-yearly 'special' survey to maintain the certification/approval.

ROLES AND RESPONSIBILITIES OF MARINE CO-ORDINATORS, MASTERS AND CREWS

A **Marine Co-ordinator** co-ordinates all the activities related to a vessel's arrival, mooring, cargo loading/discharge, and departure. This is the marine equivalent of a logistics co-ordinator. Liaison with other functions will also be involved, e.g. when vessels require annual/special independent inspections.

A **Ship's Master** (i.e. captain) has ultimate authority and responsibility aboard ship. In particular, he is responsible to the flag state, classification society and operator for the continued seaworthiness and safety of the vessel and will have the authority to do whatever is needed to maintain compliance. He is responsible for the safe navigation of the ship and the continued safety of his crew and the cargo (including from threats such as pirates). In case of incidents (such as collisions, pollution) the master must keep accurate records/logs and provide these to (and co-operate with) investigators. While, in practice, the master will delegate many tasks (such as piloting), he cannot delegate the legal responsibility laid down in international maritime law.

The crew is everyone else. There are many different ranks and departments.

Deck crew consists of:

- **Chief Officer/First Officer** (second in command after the master) – responsibilities include maintenance of the ship (the integrity of the hull, as well as equipment for the likes of fire-fighting), supervision and training of the deck crew and anything to do with the cargo (charging/discharging and cleaning tanks).
- **Second Officer** – mainly responsible for vessel navigation (course charting, etc.) but may also assist the chief officer in their duties.
- **Third Officer** – usually responsible for safety, so in charge of the safety equipment.
- **Deck Cadet** – essentially a trainee officer.
- **Able Seaman** – duties include watchman and maintaining a steady heading at the helm (as directed).
- **Ordinary Seaman** – general duties include painting, cleaning and helping with cargo operations.

Engineering crew consists of:

- **Chief Engineer** – responsible for supervising the engine room operations and other engineering equipment. There is a whole range of lower-ranking engineers (second, third, fourth) who are responsible for maintenance.

Steward's crew consists of:

- **Chief Steward** – in charge of the food and cleaning services. The Chief Cook will report to this rank.

PERSONNEL TRANSFERS AND BOARDING ARRANGEMENTS

Typical methods for personnel transfer and boarding include:

- Helicopter, but this depends on weather, location and whether the vessel is fitted with a helideck.
- Transfer basket (there are numerous designs, e.g. a personnel transfer capsule) but essentially this consists of a frame (of rope or rigid construction) inside which (or onto which) several personnel sit or hold. The basket is transferred from ship to ship using the ship's crane. There has been a number of accidents with this type of transfer and so it is not generally recommended if alternatives are available. Since this is a lifting operation, using lifting equipment and greatly affected by weather conditions, etc. it will be subject to the usual lift planning and equipment inspection, testing and marking (SWL – safe working load).

Personnel transfer capsule

- Gangways, bridges and accommodation ladders – the usual means of transfer between ship and shore where a ship is moored at port. They may also be used for transfer between offshore installations and ships. Bridges can be lifted at short notice if, for example, the weather conditions deteriorate.
- Rope ladder (for pilot transfer) - before docking at a terminal, local pilots may be transferred to the ship to aid navigation (they will be considerably more familiar with local waters). These personnel are usually transferred out at sea from a small pilot boat to the ship via a rope ladder hung over the side of the ship (this is a very common method for any ship-to-ship transfer at sea in the absence of a helicopter). This can be somewhat hazardous, so standards have been developed for the ladders and the transfer procedure itself.

Marine Transport

Security

One additional consideration is security. Vessels and terminals used by the oil and gas industries are hazardous but also obvious targets for terrorists and pirates. Personnel transfers are therefore restricted to authorised personnel only. The level of security will depend on an assessment of the perceived threat at any time, and protocols agreed between vessel and terminal and between vessels (for ship-to-ship transfers). There are three levels of security assessment, Level 1 being the lowest and Level 3 the highest.

In general, a terminal will develop a **port facility security plan** (PFSP) to cover port-ship transfers. Amongst other things, it will include measures to:

- Prevent unauthorised access to the port (and specific restricted areas).
- Allow shore leave.
- Rotate the crew.
- Allow visitors on board.

This may typically be by some form of identification, e.g. visitor badge/access card system together with enforcement by security guards. Port terminals request information about the ship, ship's personnel and cargo prior to entry to the port. They communicate and formally agree the specific security protocol for transfers.

MORE...

More detailed information on personnel transfer and boarding can be found at:

Guidance on the Transfer of Personnel to and from Offshore Vessels

(www.imca-int.com/documents/core/sel/docs/IMCASEL025.pdf)

Guidance For Oil Terminal Operators On The IMO International Ship And Port Facility Security Code

Shipping Industry Guidance on the Rigging of Ladders for Pilot Transfer

(www.impahq.org)

PERSONAL PROTECTIVE EQUIPMENT SUITABILITY

The nature of the task and its associated risk will determine the selection, suitability and appropriateness of the PPE to be worn. Typical protection worn on board ship would include safety boots, boiler suits/overalls and gloves (cotton rigger gloves for general work but also specialist gloves such as for welding or working with chemicals/oils) and high-visibility jackets. Depending on the job, personnel might also require goggles, hearing protection (engine rooms), harness and lanyard (for maintenance work at heights), respirators, breathing apparatus (including emergency escape BA), visors/face shields (for chemicals and those used for welding), and anti-static/spark-proof clothing/zips.

As an example, for ship transfers by basket, personnel might be wearing safety helmets, inflatable life jackets (with light and whistle) and survival suits (in cold seas).

DIVER OPERATIONS

Diving operations may be required for purposes of inspection (e.g. of moorings, pipelines, anchor), maintenance, repair and also decommissioning.

Diving can be categorised into several different types.

- **Surface-supplied diving** - where divers have their air supplied via hose (called an 'umbilical') from a diving support vessel or installation on the surface.
- **Self-contained underwater breathing apparatus** (SCUBA) - where the diver carries their own air supply in tanks on their back. This gives more freedom to the diver but has a more limited air supply (among other drawbacks).
- **A hybrid system** (sometimes called mobile (or portable) surface-supplied diving) - a mobile system which adds some of the greater flexibility inherent in SCUBA, but the air is actually surface-supplied.

Atmospheric diving suits and habitats may also be employed in diving operations.

Inspection is increasingly being done by remote operated vehicles (ROV – essentially a robotic underwater CCTV camera) rather than divers.

Installations would normally maintain a Site Information Dossier (SID), which would assess the likely mutual impacts and act as a source of information to diving/ROV contractors.

OGP Report 411 breaks the diving operation management process down into four steps:

COMPLIANCE

- All parties should comply with all applicable national, international, industry and company/contractor requirements for the diving operation. The most stringent requirements should be followed where there is conflict between those requirements.

PLANNING

The diving operation should be properly planned, including coverage of such activities as:

- Agreeing communications, roles and responsibilities.
- Agreeing the scope of the job to be done.
- Identifying likely hazards and assessing risks:
  - Typically, using thorough, detailed systematic techniques such as HAZID and FMEA to help identify potential domino effects.
  - OGP Report 411 breaks subsea risk assessment down into three stages:

    Stage 1 - onshore risk assessment (during the onshore planning stage).

    Stage 2 - onsite risk assessment (actually onsite and by those supervising the work – this will be more specific than the onshore assessment).

    Stage 3 - toolbox talk – a communications and review event shortly before the work actually begins involving everyone who is part of the job.

Stages 2 and 3 are generally included as part of the Execution step (later).

Divers and ROVs are obviously at risk from operations undertaken on board vessels and installations, but the reverse is also true (e.g. a diver may accidentally sever or damage an oil pipeline, or block a firewater intake).

The risks to divers include: drowning; becoming trapped (e.g. by their own airlines or by moorings, or stuck in a soft seabed); problems with their breathing apparatus (e.g. faulty valves, incorrect gas mixture, loss of gas); developing illness during the dive; blackouts; developing decompression sickness ('the bends'); developing nitrogen narcosis (a state similar to alcohol intoxication); developing oxygen poisoning; miscommunications (leading to errors); collisions (e.g. if a vessel escapes from its mooring or from an ROV also being used); the effects of extreme environment (changeable weather, cold).

- Identifying required competence (and how that will be delivered (training, etc.) and assessed (qualifications, experience validation)).

- Checking that systems, equipment and vessels are in satisfactory condition and good working order (such as through inspection or audit and validation of certificates).
- Planning for emergency situations that might arise (e.g. injured diver, decompression sickness, hyperbaric evacuation) and notification of accidents to regulators (as required by law).
- Management of change (authorisation).

EXECUTION

- Site rules must be followed/developed.
- Risk assessment (Stages 2 and 3 as discussed earlier – onsite risk assessment and toolbox talk).
- Safety briefings (inductions, expectations, etc).
- Use of formal permit-to-work/permit-to-dive system to control the dive – to ensure joint planning, risk assessment, management and communication between all parties.

MEASURING AND IMPROVING

- Review of the operation and any incidents, and what lessons can be learned.

MORE...

To view the full *Diving Recommended Practice*, OGP Report 411, go to:

www.ogp.org.uk/pubs/411.pdf

REVISION QUESTIONS

1. Outline what is meant by the term 'flagging', when applied to vessels.

2. Outline the options for personnel transfer and boarding methods.

3. Outline the four steps of the diving operation management process.

(Suggested Answers are at the end.)

Land Transport

GLOSSARY

TANKERS

Sometimes referred to as 'fixed tanks' or road tank vehicles; the tank is permanently fixed to the vehicle chassis. Tank containers (sometimes called 'ISO tanks' or 'portable tanks'), are held in boxed-steel framework. The framework is locked to the vehicle chassis but can be unloaded from the vehicle – this is particularly suited to transfer of tanks between, say, road vehicle and train, or road vehicle and ship.

ROAD TANKERS

UN Classification and Transport of Hazardous Materials (Transport of Dangerous Goods)

Carrying goods by road involves the risk of traffic accidents. If the goods carried are dangerous, there is also the risk that the dangerous goods may escape owing to collisions (with vehicles, storage vessels), or spillage of the goods (including during transfer), leading to effects such as fire, explosion, injury/death, ill health and environmental pollution.

Transportation of dangerous goods has long been subject to (or at least influenced by) international agreements. The current rules derive from a system of model regulations developed by the United Nations (UN). These are published as the *UN Recommendations on the Transport of Dangerous Goods – Model Regulations* (often referred to as the **Orange Book**, because of the colour of the cover). It is supported by the *Manual of Tests and Criteria*.

In the main, these recommendations have been adopted wholesale into legally-binding international agreements. There are modal variations (published separately) for road, rail, air, sea and inland waterway (necessitated by the operational differences). There are also some negotiated national and regional variations in their application (usually leading to more stringent requirements).

In Europe, international road transportation of dangerous goods, such as petroleum products in road tankers, is governed by a set of rules called the *European Agreement Concerning the International Carriage of Dangerous Goods by Road* (known as ADR, which derives from its French title). This is a modal (i.e. just for roads in this case) implementation of the generic UN Recommendations. National implementations by European states for purely domestic transport essentially reference ADR, but with small variations (called derogations). For example, the UK's domestic regulations are the **Carriage of Dangerous Goods and Use of Transportable Pressure Equipment Regulations 2009** and these allow use of modified marking and placarding of road tankers (see later).

Dangerous goods are substances (and articles containing them) that have been tested and assessed against agreed criteria and found to be potentially dangerous (hazardous) when carried. They are placed in recognised categories or classes; this process is called **classification**.

Dangerous goods are assigned to the following different UN classes depending on their predominant hazard:

1.	Explosive substances and articles.
2.	Gases.
3.	Flammable liquids.
4.1	Flammable solids, self-reactive substances and solid desensitised explosives.
4.2	Substances liable to spontaneous combustion.
4.3	Substances, which, in contact with water, emit flammable gases.
5.1	Oxidising substances.
5.2	Organic peroxides.
6.1	Toxic substances.
6.2	Infectious substances.
7.	Radioactive material.
8.	Corrosive substances.
9.	Miscellaneous dangerous substances and articles.

You will note that petrol is assigned to Class 3 (flammable liquids).

Taking ADR as a typical example of UN requirements for road transport of dangerous goods, it covers the following basic areas:

- General provisions – covering, for example, definitions, general training, safety obligations, appointment of safety advisers (specifically to advise on dangerous goods transportation), security.
- Classification (the allocation of dangerous goods to a class and assigning a UN number, description and packing group based on its properties).

- Dangerous goods list – effectively a very large look-up table consisting of a tabulated list of dangerous goods, together with their classes, UN number, packing and tank provisions (i.e. allowable packaging and whether it can be transported in tanks), labelling, exemptions, quantity and other restrictions and so on. The table uses codes to refer the reader to other chapters of the rules (such as packing and tank provisions) to find the detailed requirements.

GLOSSARY

UN NUMBER

A four-digit short code assigned to each entry in the list of dangerous goods (which is usually organised in UN numerical order), e.g. petrol (gasoline or motor spirit) is assigned UN number 1203. The numbers have no systematic meaning in themselves, except that anything starting with a zero is in Class 1 (explosives).

PACKING GROUP

An attempt to categorise substances into degrees of danger. There are three such groups and each is conventionally written in roman numerals. Packing group I is high danger, II is medium danger, and III is low danger. Different UN classes have different criteria for this assignment. Petrol (UN 1203) is assigned packing group II.

HAZARD IDENTIFICATION NUMBER (HIN)

A two or three-digit code, which attempts to communicate the nature and intensity of the hazard class. For example, UN 1203 (petrol) is associated with an HIN of 33 (note that this system is related to the UN hazard class – petrol is in Class 3).

EMERGENCY ACTION CODE (EAC)

A code used in the UK instead of the HIN. It communicates emergency information to fire-fighters.

PLACARDING

The display of large hazard-warning diamonds (which contain graphics communicating the hazardous nature of the load, related to the UN hazard class(es) into which the dangerous goods fall).

MARKING

When used in relation to vehicles and tanks, is the display of orange reflectorised rectangular plates. The exact nature of these depends on the type of vehicle and the type/amount of the load.

Land Transport

- Consignment procedures – marking and labelling of packages, marking and placarding of vehicles and tanks, documentation (dangerous goods transport document, container packing certificate and "instructions in writing" in case of emergency).
- Construction and testing of packaging, tanks, etc.
- Conditions of carriage, loading, unloading and handling, e.g. prohibition of smoking, precautions against electrostatic discharge.
- Vehicle crew, equipment, operation and documentation, e.g. specific training of crew, supervision of vehicles.
- Construction and approval of vehicles (such as tankers).

Road tankers carrying dangerous goods have to be marked and placarded. They must also display other information such as the UN number and the Hazard Identification Number (HIN) relating to the dangerous goods being carried. For UK domestic transport (rather than international) it is permissible to use an emergency action code (EAC) instead of the HIN. All this information may be displayed in a special panel, commonly called a "HazChem" panel. Here's an example of such information on a petrol tanker.

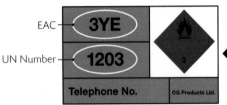

The telephone number is for specialist advice. Note the UN Class 3 (flammable liquid) placard and the additional environmentally hazardous substance pictogram (dead tree and fish). This is required if the product meets certain criteria as a pollutant.

Protection of Plant Against Vehicles Striking Plant

Vulnerable plant and equipment, such as bulk storage tanks, should be protected from vehicle collision damage. This may typically be achieved either by position (the storage tank is isolated from the tanker off-loading point) or by barriers (e.g. Armco metal barriers, as routinely used on motorways/ highways). A bund wall should not be used as collision protection – the bund wall itself should be further protected with a barrier, if necessary.

Driver Training

ADR requires drivers of tankers carrying dangerous goods to attend a vocational course of instruction (theory and practice) and sit an externally assessed examination – for the classes of goods being carried. This gives them a certificate of competency, which has to be updated at specific intervals.

The course covers some general aspects of dangerous goods transportation but, for tanker drivers, will also cover tanker-specific issues, such as:

- Vehicle behaviour (e.g. load movement/surge).
- Specific vehicle requirements.
- Filling and discharge.
- Specific rules (approval certificates, marking, placarding, etc).

Loading and Unloading Arrangements

Drivers of tankers must be fully informed of the dangers of the materials carried and the emergency action that needs to be taken. ADR requires drivers to carry 'instructions in writing', more commonly known as the TRansport EMergency card (TREM card). This is a four-page instruction, which, among other things, describes the nature of the hazardous load and action to be taken in an emergency. The TREM card must be kept in the vehicle cab so that it can be easily located by the emergency services in the event of an accident. The driver and the recipient of materials should have written procedures that set out the precautions that need to be taken during loading and unloading. Fire extinguishers should be carried on all vehicles. If substances are flammable or explosive, earth connections should be used during loading and unloading to prevent the possibility of a static spark, and no other sources of ignition, such as smoking materials, should be allowed in the vicinity.

Where bulk storage tanks are used for different substances, there is always the possibility of cross contamination, i.e. a substance being unloaded from a tanker into the wrong bulk tank at an installation. This can be prevented by strict operating procedures and the use of couplings of a different design for each substance. It is also important to ensure that tanks to be filled have enough space so as to prevent spillage through overfilling.

TOPIC FOCUS

Filling road tankers involves the risk of fire and explosion if a flammable mixture of fuel and air can be generated above the explosive limits in the presence of an ignition source.

Consequently, control measures need to be in place to:

- Prevent the formation of a flammable mixture of fuel and air:
    - Vapour return systems to reduce flammable vapour release.
    - Adequate tank space to prevent spillage through overfilling.
    - Level monitoring with alarms.
    - Nitrogen blanketing of the road tanker and the bulk storage tank.
    - Monitoring equipment to detect leaks from the tank and associated (buried) pipework.
    - Strict operating procedures to prevent leaks and spills.
- Control potential ignition sources:
    - Prohibition of smoking.
    - Zoning of the filling area and electrical equipment appropriate for that zone.

- Reduce the risk of ignition by static electricity by:
    - Control of pumping rates.
    - Proper pipe sizing to keep liquid velocities low.
    - Elimination of splash filling and free-fall of flammable liquids by:
        - Lowering fill velocities.
        - Directing the discharge of liquid down the side of the vessel.
        - Submerging fill pipes below the liquid level in the vessel.
    - Avoiding the use of filters or installing filters far enough upstream of discharge points to allow adequate time for any static generated to leak away.
    - Use of antistatic footwear and clothing.
    - Earthing of pipeline, vehicle and tank.
    - Electrical bonding of all pipe joints and of the pipeline to the tanker.
- Deal with emergencies:
    - Fire extinguishers to deal with any small outbreaks of fire on, or in the immediate vicinity of, the fuelling unit.
    - Dry sand or other absorbent material to aid the clearing up of small leaks or spills.

We have already considered methods of filling tanks and their safety implications (Element 3) and these principles apply to loading road tankers as well:

- 'Top' filling can create 'splash', aerating the substance and creating a large electrostatic charge, as well as allowing the release of vapours. It also requires the driver to work at a height on the top of the tanker. Consequently, the fill pipe should touch the bottom of the tanker compartment, the vehicle should be earthed and the driver protected from a fall from height.
- 'Bottom' filling through a closed system alleviates the problem of vapour escape, but relies on pressure venting and relief devices to be functioning properly. Consequently, the overfill protection system needs to be effective and the tanker compartment correctly sized for the cargo.

Bottom loading of petrol tankers is the main method used for loading petrol in order to facilitate vapour recovery to prevent the release of hydrocarbon vapours and to avoid the need to access the top of the tanker.

Land Transport

TRAFFIC MANAGEMENT

On Site

The principles for on-site management of traffic include:

- Minimise bends/junctions, steep gradients and the need for reversing.
- Pedestrian and vehicle segregation – clearly designate areas for pedestrian walkways and crossing points.
- Clear signage (which, as far as possible, reflects standard road signage) – warning of speed limits, obstructions, allowable width/height, etc.
- Well lit (if necessary) during hours of darkness.
- Wide enough for the vehicles and, if not, consider one-way systems.
- Enforce speed limits.
- Protect vulnerable plant with barriers.
- Designed with plenty of space for off-loading (demountable tanks).
- Dedicated tanker off-loading points (with emergency facilities and environmental protection built in).
- Security access gate/sign in (so you know who is on site and control who enters the site).

Routes

It goes without saying that not all routes are suitable for vehicles, such as tankers transporting petroleum products, e.g. narrow roads, weak bridges. There is also the issue of the security threat (terrorism, theft) to the valuable load being carried and its possible use as a terrorist weapon. Consideration of the security of dangerous goods is a specific requirement of the UN Recommendations and, therefore, ADR.

Routes should be planned to minimise such threats (and obstructions). It is not generally considered a good idea to use the same route each time (predictability). However, although the route should be varied, it should be planned each time, the advantage being that if the vehicle goes off route, it can be detected (especially with the more commonly available vehicle tracking systems).

RAIL

Rail transportation of petroleum products will involve tank cars and tank containers. Modal rules on transport of dangerous goods derive from the UN Recommendations and rail is no exception. In Europe, the implementation is called the **Regulations Concerning the International Carriage of Dangerous Goods by Rail** (RID).

Earlier, we discussed the ADR requirements for road transport of dangerous goods in tankers; there are very similar risks for rail. As a result, the requirements are very similar, the general layout and thrust of the two modal regulatory texts being alike. There are some obvious operational differences and there are greater restrictions than for road, and especially when transporting dangerous goods through long tunnels (such as the Channel Tunnel).

REVISION QUESTIONS

4. Outline the general requirements for dangerous goods tanker-driver training.

5. Outline why it might be important to plan the route of a road tanker carrying dangerous goods.

(Suggested Answers are at the end.)

SUMMARY

This final element has dealt with logistics and transport operations. In particular, it has:

- Discussed the hazards of working on marine vessels, such as FPSOs. These hazards include extremes of weather, which could, for example, cause a vessel to come loose from its moorings; accelerated wear and corrosion (from salt spray); the proximity of other vessels (leading to potential collisions); hazardous substances (flammable, toxic and environmentally hazardous); cargo and personnel transfer operations; and piracy.

- Noted the difficulties associated with the loading/unloading of cargo at marine terminals. The potential for fire and explosion is obvious and precautions include electrical isolation of the ship from the shore, as well as secure mooring and prevention of unauthorised access.

- Explained vessel and crew regulation under a system known as 'flagging', which includes certification, approval and continued maintenance of the vessel.

- Noted the vessel crew hierarchy – the Master (captain) is in ultimate control of the vessel and crew but has an array of subordinates, divided into deck crew (e.g. First Officer), engineering crew (e.g. Second Engineer) and steward's crew (e.g. Chief Cook).

- Discussed personnel transfers, which are conducted using a variety of methods such as helicopters, bridges, gangways, transfer baskets and rope ladders.

- Highlighted PPE requirements, which are dependent on the task but would typically include hard hat, boiler suit, hi-viz vest, safety boots and gloves.

- Explained the management of diving operations using a four-step approach: compliance (with regulations and other requirements); planning (onshore risk assessment, communications, checking competence, etc.); execution (on-site risk assessment, site rules, permit-to-dive, etc); and measuring and improving (reviewing and learning from incidents).

- Explained the basics of the UN system of model regulations for dangerous goods transportation (the UN classes, list of dangerous goods, the meaning of UN numbers, marking and placarding of tanks, etc).

- Discussed the use of road tankers to transport petroleum products and the precautions required during their loading/unloading (e.g. against fire/explosion, role of TREM cards).

- Noted the requirement for vocational training of road tanker drivers.

- Discussed the management of onsite traffic, e.g. vehicle and pedestrian segregation and speed limits.

- Highlighted the need for security arrangements for tankers, such as the planning of varied routes to reduce the likelihood of hijack and use in a terrorist attack.

- Considered rail transportation, noting that it has similar requirements to the road transportation of dangerous goods, both being based on UN recommendations.

Exam Skills

QUESTION

(a) Identify three risks associated with offshore diving operations. (3)

(a) Identify suitable controls to minimise offshore diving operation risks. (5)

APPROACHING THE QUESTION

- Using the system we have covered, the first thing to do is read the question carefully. There are two parts to this question, and in both you are asked to 'identify' – in this case risks and controls. You should structure your approach (a bullet-point list can be used to relate the issues) and expand afterwards, as 'identify' needs more than just a 'list'.

- Next, consider the marks available. In this question there are two parts giving eight marks; question (a) awards three marks and (b) awards five.

- The question should take around eight minutes.

- Now highlight the key words. In this case, it might look like this:

  a) Identify three risks associated with offshore diving operations. (3)
  b) Identify suitable controls to minimise offshore diving operation risks. (5)

- Read the question again – make sure you understand it.

- Following this, the next stage is to develop a plan. Remember, a plan can be completed in various ways, but it could consist of the following:

SUGGESTED ANSWER

Plan

The question requires	Answers include
3 risks in diving	Drowning Becoming trapped Problems with SCUBA Illness during dive Collisions Effects of environment Water (poor) visibility Seismic operations Simultaneous operations
Controls to minimise diving risks	Communications Identification of all hazards Diving plan in place (essential) Assess the risks Competence of divers Equipment and vessel safety checks Plan for possible emergencies Adequate staff numbers Safety briefings and training Permit-to-work system in use

Now have a go at the question yourself.

Exam Skills

POSSIBLE ANSWER BY EXAM CANDIDATE

(a) Three risks associated with diving operations are:

- Divers and others involved could drown.
- Divers could become trapped, e.g. by their own airlines or by moorings, or become stuck in a soft seabed.
- Divers could encounter problems with their breathing apparatus, such as faulty demand valves, incorrect gas mixture, loss of gas.
- Divers could develop illness during the dive, such as blackouts, decompression sickness, nitrogen narcosis, or oxygen poisoning.
- There could be communication errors leading to mistakes being made.
- Collisions could occur, e.g. a vessel escaping from its moorings, or from an ROV in use.
- The effects of extreme environment, such as rough seas, changeable weather, cold, poor visibility in the water.
- Seismic operations or simultaneous operations in the area of the dive.

Remember, only THREE risks were asked for – the additional ones are given as examples.

(b) Suitable controls to minimise the risks in offshore diving operations include:

- Set up and agree a common communication system practised and understood by all involved (including between surface and underwater crews).
- Agree roles and responsibilities of all parties (surface and underwater).
- Identify all hazards of the area and the dive.
- Carry out suitable and sufficient assessment of the risks associated with the hazards identified.
- Put in place a comprehensive diving plan.
- Identify and validate the qualifications, experience and competence of all divers and other participants, including boat crews.
- Carry out safety checks on the diving and breathing equipment.
- Carry out safety checks on the diving and support vessels involved in the operation.
- Take account of possible emergencies and formulate a plan.
- Ensure adequate rescue and recovery equipment available for emergencies.
- Ensure adequate staff for normal operations and emergencies.
- Carry out safety briefings.
- Use permits-to-work to identify and control the risks.
- Monitor weather (meteorological and oceanographic) reports.

REASONS FOR POOR MARKS ACHIEVED BY CANDIDATES IN EXAM

- Not answering the question at all. If you do not attempt all questions required you cannot get any marks.
- Not following a structured approach: remember, the question is in two parts. The question asked you to identify, so a list for parts (a) and (b) would not gain maximum marks.
- Giving lots of other information not relevant to the question.

REVISION AND EXAMINATION

THE LAST HURDLE

Now that you have worked your way through the book, this section will help you prepare for your NEBOSH examination. This guide contains useful advice and guidance on how to approach your revision and the exam itself.

Revision and Examination

YOUR IOG1 EXAM

The NEBOSH examination will consist of one question paper, which contains one 20-mark question and ten 8-mark questions. You are allowed two hours in which to complete the exam paper and you should answer all the questions.

To pass the IOG1 exam, you must obtain a minimum of 45% of the total marks available.

If your performance is less than the pass mark then you will be "referred". This means you may resit the examination providing you do so within **five years** of the original sitting. You may resit as many times as you want within that five-year timescale.

Be Prepared

It may be some time since you last took an exam.

Remember, success in an exam depends mainly on:

- **Revision** – you have to be able to remember, recall and apply the information contained in your course materials; and
- **Exam technique** – you have to be able to understand the questions and write good answers in the time available.

Revision and exam technique are skills that can be learned. We will now look at both of these skills so you can prepare yourself for the exam. There is a saying that "proper planning and preparation prevents a poor performance". This is especially true in the case of exams.

REVISION TIPS

Using this textbook

You should read through all of the topics at least once before beginning your revision in earnest. This first read-through should be done slowly and carefully.

Having completed this first revision reading of the course textbook consider briefly reviewing all of it again to check that you understand all of the elements and the important principles that they contain. At this stage, you are not trying to memorise information but simply checking your understanding of the concepts.

Remember that *understanding* the information and being able to *remember and recall* it are two different things. As you read the book you should **understand** it; in the exam you have to be able to **remember, recall** and **apply** it. To do this successfully most people have to go back over the material repeatedly.

Re-read the book and make notes that summarise important information from each element. You could use index cards and create a portable, quick and easy revision aid.

Pay attention to the **Key Information** and **Topic Focus** boxes in this text, but do be aware that these only summarise some of the important points and focus on particular topics. They do not represent the only information that you need to remember.

Check your basic knowledge content of each element by reading the **Summary**. The Summary should help you recall the ideas contained in the text. If it does not, then you may need to revisit the appropriate sections of the element.

Using the Syllabus Guide

We recommend that you purchase a copy of the NEBOSH Guide to the International Technical Certificate in Oil and Gas Operational Safety, which contains the syllabus for your exam. If a topic is in the syllabus then it is possible that there will be an examination question on that topic.

Map your level of knowledge and recall against the syllabus guide. Look at the **Content** listed for each element in the syllabus guide. Ask yourself the following question:

If there is a question in the exam about that topic, could I answer it?

You can even score your current level of knowledge for each topic in each element of the syllabus guide and then use your scores as an indication of your personal strengths and weaknesses. For example, if you scored yourself as 5 out of 5 for the topic **Learning from Incidents** in Element 1, then obviously you don't have much work to do on that subject as you approach the exam. But if you scored yourself at 2 out of 5 for the topic **Safe Containment of Hydrocarbons** in Element 3 then you have identified an area of weakness. Having identified your strengths and weaknesses in this way you can use this information to decide on the topic areas that you need to concentrate on as you revise for the exam.

You could also annotate or highlight sections of the text which you think are important.

Another way of using the syllabus guide is as an active revision aid:

- Pick a topic at random from any of the IOG1 elements.
- Write down as many facts and ideas that you can recall that are relevant to that particular topic.

Go back to your book and see what you missed, and fill in the missing areas.

EXAM HINTS

Success in the exam depends on averaging around half marks or more for each question. Marks are awarded for setting down ideas that are relevant **to the question asked** and demonstrating that you understand what you are talking about. If you have studied this textbook thoroughly then this should not be a problem.

One common mistake in answering questions is to go into too much detail on specific topics and fail to deal with the wider issues. If you only cover half the relevant issues, you can only achieve half of the available marks. Try to give as wide an answer as you can, without stepping outside the subject matter of the question altogether. Make sure that you cover each issue in appropriate detail in order to demonstrate that you have the relevant knowledge. Giving relevant examples is a good way of doing this.

We mentioned earlier the value of using the syllabus to plan your revision. Another useful way of combining syllabus study with examination practice is to create your own exam questions by adding one of the words you might find at the beginning of an exam question (such as 'explain' or 'identify' or 'outline') in front of the syllabus topic areas. In this way, you can produce a whole range of questions similar to those used in the exam.

Revision and Examination Guide

BEFORE THE EXAM

You should:

- Know where the exam is to take place.
- Arrive in good time.
- Bring your examination entry voucher, which includes your candidate number, photographic proof of identity, pens, pencils, ruler, etc. (Remember, these must be in a clear plastic bag or wallet.)
- Bring water to drink and sweets to suck, if you want to.

DURING THE EXAM

- Read through the whole exam paper before starting work if that will help settle your nerves. Start with the question of your choice.
- Manage your time. The exam is two hours long. You should attempt to answer all 11 questions in the two hours. To do this you might spend:
  - 25-30 minutes answering Question 1 (worth 20 marks), and then
  - 8-9 minutes on each of the ten remaining 8-mark questions.

  Check the clock regularly as you write your answers. You should always know exactly where you are with regard to time.
- As you start each question read the question carefully. Pay particular attention to the wording of the question to make sure you understand what the examiner is looking for. Note the verbs (command words), such as 'describe', 'explain', 'identify', or 'outline' that are used in the question. These indicate the amount of depth and detail required in your answer. As a general guide:
  - 'Explain' and 'describe' mean give an understanding of/a detailed account of something.
  - 'Outline' means give the key features of something.
  - 'Identify' means give a reference to something (could be name or title).
- Pay close attention to the number of marks available for each question or part of a question – this usually indicates how many key pieces of information the examiner expects to see in your answer.
- Give examples wherever possible, based either on your own personal experience, or things you have read about. An example can be used to illustrate an idea and demonstrate that you understand what you are saying.
- If you start to run out of time, write your answers in bullet point or checklist style, rather than failing to answer a question at all.
- Keep your handwriting under control; if the examiner cannot read what you have written, then he or she cannot mark it.
- You will not be penalised for poor grammar or spelling, as long as your answers are clear and can be understood. However, you may lose marks if the examiner cannot make sense of the sentence that you have written.

SUGGESTED ANSWERS

NO PEEKING!

Once you have worked your way through the revision questions in this book, use the suggested answers on the following pages to find out where you went wrong (and what you got right), and as a resource to improve your knowledge and question-answering technique.

Element 1 Health, Safety and Environmental Management in Context

Question 1

- To identify the immediate and root causes of the incident – incidents are usually caused by unsafe acts and unsafe conditions in the workplace, but these often arise from underlying or root causes.
- To identify corrective actions that will prevent a recurrence – the main reason for investigating.

Question 2

Step 1: Gather factual information about the event.

Step 2: Analyse that information and draw conclusions about the immediate and root causes.

Step 3: Identify suitable corrective measures.

Step 4: Plan the remedial actions.

Question 3

A simple investigation might be carried out by the line manager of the area; a more detailed investigation often involves a team of investigators, which might include:

- A safety specialist.
- Senior managers.
- A technical specialist.
- A worker representative.

Offshore investigating teams may also include installation specialists from services such as drilling, well services, maintenance, process, and deck crews.

Question 4

Various documents may be examined during an accident investigation, such as:

- Company policy.
- Risk assessments.
- Training records.
- Safe systems of work.
- Permits-to-work.
- Maintenance records.
- Disciplinary records.
- Internal accident-report forms.
- Log-book entries.
- Computer printouts relevant to the situation.

Question 5

Immediate causes are the unsafe acts and unsafe conditions that gave rise to the event itself. These will be the things that occurred at the time and place of the accident. For example, a worker slips on a patch of oil spilt on the floor – immediate causes: the slip hazard (unsafe condition), the worker walking through it (unsafe act).

Question 6

Immediate causes for such an accident might be:

- Failure to secure the load on the pallet.
- Poor road positioning of the truck close to a pedestrian exit.
- Aggressive braking by the truck driver.
- An inattentive pedestrian stepping out in front of the truck.

On investigation, each of these immediate causes might have their own separate root causes, such as:

- No training for the driver, who is new to the workplace, has not worked with this type of load before and is unaware of the load-securing technique required.
- Lack of segregation of pedestrian and traffic routes; no barriers and no markings to separate the two.
- Lack of proper driver induction into their new workplace so they are unaware of the layout and position of pedestrian exits, etc.
- Poor maintenance of the truck.
- No refresher training for existing staff, meaning that experienced staff become complacent.

Question 7

The **lower flammable limit (LFL)** or **lower explosive limit (LEL):** the minimum concentration of fuel in air that is sufficient to allow combustion to occur. Below the LFL, the mixture is too lean to burn.

The **upper flammable limit (UFL)** or **upper explosive limit (UEL):** the maximum concentration of fuel in air that is sufficient to allow combustion to occur. Above the UFL the mixture is too rich to burn.

Question 8

Carcinogenic – can induce the growth of malignant tumours.

Question 9

The dangers of LPG lie with its flammability and explosive properties, and the fact that it is stored under great pressure, and hence very low temperatures, to retain its liquid state. On release, LPG reverts to its gaseous state, with rapid and considerable increase in volume.

Question 10

An anti-foaming agent or "defoamer" is a chemical additive that reduces and hinders the formation of foam in industrial process liquids.

Question 11

Low Specific Activity sludges (LSA sludges).

Question 12

The common elements are:

- Plan - implies having a considered policy.
- Do - concerns the arrangements for putting the plan into practice.
- Check – means it is necessary to assess or monitor performance.
- Act – means performance should be reviewed leading to continuous improvement in the management system.

Question 13

The four main areas of risk are:

- **Production workplace** – the field or rig and its associated facilities and support systems; safe access and egress; work environment; welfare facilities and accommodation; pipelines and structures; and electrical and communications installations.
- **Plant and substances** – the drilling and pumping and transportation systems of the oil and gas; how the oil and gas are stored and handled; and all materials in use at the process area.
- **Procedures** – organisational procedures such as work and shift patterns, job design and the way work is done (and managed).
- **People** – management and leadership; competence and placement of workers; training and health surveillance necessary.

Question 14

In a **bow-tie diagram** barriers are normally placed between the **initiating event** and the **release**, and the **release** and its **consequences**.

The barriers are placed to prevent, control or mitigate the outcome of the event and are known as **Lines of Defence** (LOD) or **Layers of Protection** (LOP).

Question 15

- Identification of major accident hazards.
- Evaluation of major accident risks and measures taken (or to be taken) to control those risks.
- Arrangements for audit and audit reports.
- Confirmation that an adequate safety management system is in place.
- Major accident prevention policies.
- Identification of the safety-critical elements in place to manage major accident hazards.
- Details of the emergency plan.

Element 2: Hydrocarbon Process Safety 1

Question 1

To make sure that the work that contractors do is covered by the usual methods of safe working:

- Ensure that the hazards of the contractors' job have been identified and steps taken to reduce the risks.
- Ensure that a representative of the owner or operator is available to make sure contractors follow the rules of the installation.
- Ensure that all contractor workers know who the site or installation contact person is, and how they can be contacted.
- Have procedures in place that ensure close and safe working with contractors at all times.

Question 2

Step 1 – Planning.

Step 2 – Choosing a contractor.

Step 3 – Contractors working on site.

Step 4 – Keeping a check.

Step 5 – Reviewing the work.

Question 3

The Dow Fire and Explosion Index is a rapid hazard-assessment method for use on chemical plant during process and plant development, and in the design of plant layout.

Question 4

Permits-to-work detail and explain:

- The work involved.
- The isolations required.
- Hazards in the work to be carried out.
- Precautions to avoid injury.

Question 5

Six areas where a permit might be required are:

- Hot work (welding, burning, grinding, etc).
- Live or high-voltage work.
- Working at height.
- Working over water.
- Work in confined spaces.
- Special permits for work carried out under special conditions (usually maintenance work of a non-routine nature).

Question 6

Safe isolation systems are concerned with the safe isolation of (**only four required**):

- Hydraulic (oil) power.
- Pneumatic power and stored energy.
- Residual energy.
- Combustion engines.
- Natural gravitational forces/weight.
- Steam or high-pressure water systems.
- Any combinations of or additions to the above.

Question 7

Safe isolation - the interruption, disconnection and separation of **all** the equipment's motive power sources in such a way that this disconnection and separation is **secure by lockable means**.

Question 8

Shift hand-over should be:

- High priority, conducted face-to-face.
- Two-way with both participants taking joint responsibility.
- Carried out using verbal and written communication.
- Based on analysis of the information needs of the oncoming shift staff.
- Given as much time as necessary.

Question 9

Ineffective communications come about from a variety of causes (**only four required**):

- Some information is missed or missing.
- Unnecessary information is included, causing confusion.
- Information is inaccurate or misleading.
- The quality of information is poor.
- Information is not understood (either by transmitter or receiver).
- Information is not carried forward over successive shifts.

Question 10

The most problems in communication occur:

- During plant maintenance, when it runs across more than one shift.
- In areas where safety systems may have been over-ridden (e.g. fire deluge system switched to manual).
- During deviations from normal working, such as breakdowns, or lack of spares.
- When members of the team have been absent from work for long periods.
- If handover takes place between experienced and inexperienced staff.

Question 11

Corrosion control practices and procedures include (**only four required**):

- Selection of materials: steels, corrosion-resistant alloys, plastics.
- Chemical treatments: biocides and corrosion inhibitors.
- Surface coatings: metallic, non-metallic and paints / organic coatings.
- Cathodic protection: galvanising and impressed current.
- Process and environmental controls: control of through-put, dehumidification.
- Initial design: safe concept, engineering and detail reviews, life-cycle implications and corrosion risks.

Question 12

The four critical areas that risk-based inspection schemes are based on are:

- Ensure the risks are reduced to ALARP.
- Optimise the inspection schedules.
- Inspect the most critical items of plant, equipment and components.
- Use the most appropriate inspection methods.

Question 13

Ignition sources are (**select four from**):

- **Electrical equipment** - routinely inspect and test to prevent faults developing that could cause sparks and overheating.
- **Hot work** (welding, burning, etc.) - control with a permit-to-work when done in sensitive areas.
- **Smoking** - control and limit to restricted areas on site (welfare areas).
- **Cooking and heating appliances** - locate safely (confine to a galley offshore) and use carefully.
- **Mechanical heat** (overheating) - control by good maintenance programmes.
- **Deliberate ignition** (arson) - prevent by good security, perimeter fences (onshore), CCTV and security lighting.

Question 14

It is vital for the safety of maintenance personnel that services are stopped, isolated, drained down, blanked, etc. and remain in a safe condition for the duration of the work. This is ensured by the work being carried out under the controls of a permit-to-work. The permit will have a completion section to ensure that all systems are put back into operable condition before start-up, to protect maintenance and operations personnel.

Element 3: Hydrocarbon Process Safety 2

Question 1

Three forces from:

- Pulling (stretching) a material - tensile force.
- Pushing into a material - compressive force.
- A force not applied in line - shear force.
- External forces can be bending forces.
- Twisting forces - axial forces.

Question 2

Creep - the gradual extension of material under a steady tensile stress, over a prolonged period of time.

Question 3

The criteria necessary for stress-corrosion cracking to occur are:

- A susceptible material.
- A corrosive environment.
- Enough tensile stress to induce the condition.

Question 4

Factors that promote brittle fracture include (**only two required**):

- **Low temperature** – can affect failure in a brittle or ductile mode. The effect is particularly important for materials that are subject to cold weather, and LPG cylinders and systems.
- **Impact or "snatch" loading** – can produce very high levels of stress very quickly, particularly in such items as lifting equipment. When subject to such loading, the material does not have time to spread the load evenly throughout the crystalline boundaries, thus producing high areas of stress. On failure in these locations the failure propagates throughout the material and total failure occurs.
- **Residual tensile stresses** – stresses "built into" the structure of the material by the fabrication or assembly processes, such as beams being pulled together, or in the vicinity of welds. These tensile stresses act within the loading, leading to brittle fracture, effectively "pre-loading" the material.
- **Inherently brittle material** – some materials have an atomic structure that has difficulty giving way under stress and will fail by brittle fracture. Such materials include cast iron, glass and ceramics.

Question 5

The advantages and disadvantages of the various NDT testing techniques are:

Test	Advantages	Disadvantages
Dye penetrant	Inexpensive and convenient. Superior to visual examination alone. For all non-porous materials.	Surface defects only. Defects must be open to the surface.
Magnetic particle	More sensitive than dye penetrant. Can also find sub-surface defects.	Ferrous metals only. Cannot find defects at any significant depth. Requires a power source.
Eddy current	Rapid detection of surface or sub-surface flaws. Can measure depth of shallow flaws.	Cannot operate close to other free surfaces, e.g. thin sheet. Cannot find deep flaws. Requires a power source.
Ultrasonic	Precise location of internal and external defects. Sizing of many defects possible.	Expensive equipment. Dependent on a skilled operator and a power supply.
Radiography	Permanent, pictorial, easily interpreted images obtained. Locates majority of internal defects.	Safety hazards (radiation). Expensive X-ray sets. Thickness limits (more so with X-rays). Power supply needed. Needs access to both sides.
Pressure testing	System can be tested while in operation.	Cleaning problem if hydraulic medium used in a gaseous system.

Question 6

All ESD systems should be separate from and independent of normal production controls so that common-cause failures can be avoided. Control valves should be independent within ESD systems and not used for dual control or shut-down, as they are not designed for tight shut-off.

Question 7

Where bypass systems are provided around shut-down valves for maintenance purposes, they should be locked closed with the shut-down valve handwheels removed. Valves on hydraulic system return lines themselves can cause failure, so should be locked open.

Question 8

Blowdown - the removal of liquid content from process vessels and equipment to reduce the likelihood of fires or explosions occurring. It is similar to depressurisation carried out in gas process systems.

Question 9

A gas flare, or flare-stack, is a tall discharge facility used to eliminate waste gas that is not required in other processes or for transportation. They can also act as safety systems for non-waste gases, venting process gases through pressure-relief systems. In emergency situations, the flare can burn out total reserve gas.

Question 10

Any three from:

- **Steam-assisted flares** – have single burner tips and are elevated above ground to burn vented gas in a diffusion flame. Most refineries and chemical plants use this type of flare. Steam is injected into the combustion zone to promote turbulence for mixing and to induce air into the flame. This ensures an adequate air supply and good mixing.
- **Air-assisted flares** – use forced air for combustion and mixing, and give a relatively smoke-free flame. The burner has many small gas orifices in a spider-shaped pattern inside at the top of a steel cylinder, and the air for combustion is provided by a fan in the bottom of the cylinder. The fan speed can vary altering the amount of air for combustion. These are handy for use where there is no steam available. They are not usually used with large flares.
- **Non-assisted flares** – a simple flare tip without any steam or air mixing facility, and limited to gas streams with a low heat content and a low ratio of hydrogen/carbon that will burn well and without producing lots of smoke. They manage with less air to give complete combustion and have lower combustion temperatures.

- **Pressure–assisted flares** – use the vent-stream pressure to assist with mixing the combustible fuels at the burner tip. Where there is enough vent-stream pressure they can be used on flare tips that would have used steam or air to give a smokeless discharge. They have a number of burner heads that operate depending on the amount of gas to be discharged. Although not exclusively, this type normally has its burner arrangement at ground level, so has to be located in a remote plant area with adequate space.
- **Enclosed ground flares** – have burner heads enclosed in an internally insulated shell, which helps cut down noise, luminosity, and heat radiation and protects from the wind. Adequate mixing is achieved by a high nozzle pressure-drop, so air or steam assistance is not needed. The height of the flare tip must be adequate to create enough draught to supply enough air to give smokeless combustion and to allow the thermal plume to disperse. These flares will always be located at ground level. They have less capacity than an open flare and work well with continuous, constant-flow vent streams.

Question 11

The main cause of the incident is thought to be the overfilling of a floating-roof gasoline tank (tank 912).

Question 12

The roof 'floats', in that it can move up and down within the outer shell of the tank, always remaining immediately above the surface of the liquid contained, minimising the air gap and potential build-up of flammable hydrocarbon vapours.

Question 13

Fixed-roof storage tanks are intended for use with liquids having very high flash points (i.e. of low volatility, such as water, bitumen, etc.).

Question 14

(a) Tanks should be surrounded by a bund to limit the spread of spillage or leakage, and should be designed to hold at least 110% of the capacity of the largest tank within the bund, making allowance for the space occupied by other tanks. In exceptional cases where there is no risk of pollution or of hazard to the public, this figure may be reduced to 75%.

(b) In the Buncefield incident the bund was around three tanks; the capacity of the bund was thought to be sufficient (110% of the largest tank), but spillage into the bund from any one tank would affect all tanks in the bund in the case of a fire. This questioned the value of common bunding rather then individual bunds for each tank.

Element 3: Hydrocarbon Process Safety 2

Question 15
- 'Top' filling is achieved through a filling-valve arrangement (usually gravity-fed) through the top of the tank. More often used with smaller tanks and containers.
- 'Bottom' filling is where the substance is delivered into the tank under pressure through a closed pipeline. This is the common method for larger tanks and road tankers.

Question 16
The three stages of decommissioning are:
- Decontamination.
- Dismantling.
- Disposal.

Question 17
The three elements of the fire triangle are:
- Oxygen.
- Heat (ignition).
- Fuel.

Question 18
The five stages of combustion are:
- **Induction**
  Heat is initially supplied by an external source, which results in production of flammable vapour. These vapours mix with air above the fuel and, if sufficient energy is provided, the combustion reaction begins between the vapour and the oxygen.
- **Ignition**
  The point of ignition is reached when the reaction becomes self-sustaining (and no longer requires an external heat source). At this stage, combustion develops very quickly and there is a dramatic increase in temperature as the fire grows.
- **Growth**
  Once ignited, the fire may spread through direct burning, or through the typical mechanisms of heat transmission (convection, conduction or radiation). The rate, scale and pattern of growth depend on a number of factors, such as: the nature, form and amount of the fuel; the availability of oxygen (open, ventilated versus sealed containment); the amount of heat produced by the reaction.
- **Steady State**
  After the growth period the temperature stabilises and the combustion process reaches a steady state where the reaction between fuel and oxygen is balanced until all the fuel is consumed.
- **Decay**
  Decay will begin when either the fuel or oxygen has been consumed. The fire will extinguish and gradually cool down. In the early stages of decay, there is still a considerable amount of heat; there is certainly enough to cause re-ignition if more fuel or oxygen is supplied. In the latter case, admission of oxygen (e.g. opening a window) into an oxygen-depleted room can result in the sudden explosive re-ignition of vapours.

Question 19
- Zone 0 or Zone 20 – Category 1 equipment.
- Zone 1 or Zone 21 – Category 1 or 2 equipment.
- Zone 2 or Zone 22 – Category 1, 2 or 3 equipment.

Question 20
The two common types of steam boilers are:
- Closed systems, in which unused condensed steam goes back through the system to be re-heated.
- Open systems, where the boiler vents unused steam from the system, usually requiring a continuous flow of water.

Closed and open boilers are also in two forms:
- Firetube boilers – (the most common type), having an outer shell (the firetube) with tubes of water inside it. Heated gases pass through the core of the firetube and heat water in the internal water tubes, which creates the steam.
- Watertube boilers – the simplest boiler, having a vertical tube above the heating source. Water enters the vertical tube and is heated until it becomes steam, which then passes out through the top of the tube.

Question 21
Flame impingement is where a flame that is used to heat the water in a boiler touches boiler surfaces, such as directly on heating coils or pipework. This can cause erosion and corrosion, cracking and failure of the materials.

Element 4: Fire Protection and Emergency Response

Question 1

Voting systems are used in order to minimise false alarms, in cases where activation has consequences such as shutting down production (you don't want that unless it is absolutely necessary, as it will cost significant time and money). The principle of operation is that more than one detector in a set must be triggered and it is in this sense that it is called a 'voting' system. They can be set to different sensitivities, depending on the risk (typically two out of three).

Question 2

- Fire-water source, e.g. sea water.
- Fire-water pump, sized to deliver the necessary pressure and flow rate and designed to be activated quickly.
- Fire-water mains – the pipework transporting the water from the pump to where it is needed; these may be normally dry or, for speedier response, wet.
- Discharge nozzles (controlled by a single valve for a given array of nozzles).

Question 3

Passive fire protection is predominantly thermally-insulating design elements that are put and left in place, like fire barriers, fire-resistant coatings and cladding. They help stop escalation of the fire and protect routes.

Active fire protection means measures that are brought into play when a fire is detected, in order to actively tackle/ extinguish the fire, e.g. fixed sprinkler installations, hoses and monitors.

Question 4

The main means of fire protection is to use fixed foam installations, which spread foam around the rim seal. Monitors and water-deluge cooling sprays may also be used.

Question 5

Basically, it is a record of a specific fire and explosion risk assessment. It would typically involve considering:

- The foreseeable fires/explosions (cellulosic, hydrocarbon pool, hydrocarbon jet).
- Their likelihood of occurrence and likely severity, which may depend on:
  - Location (accommodation, process module, helideck, etc).
  - Nature of the gas/liquid, the way in which they are being handled (temperature/pressure) and the amounts in use.
  - Complexity of the installation.
- Other related issues, such as:
  - Human factors (i.e. how people behave in a fire/explosion).
  - Remoteness of the installation (proximity of external help).

This aids selection of the most appropriate fire/explosion prevention and mitigation measures.

Question 6

- Level 1 - Basic first-aid: intended as first-line treatment to preserve life and stabilise the injured; requiring the provision of an adequate number of trained first-aiders (depending on level of risk, number of workers, installation remoteness, etc.) and first-aid equipment (first-aid kits, etc.).
- Level 2 - Advanced first-aid: requiring first-aiders with more advanced skills (such as the use of specialist equipment or methods).
- Level 3 – Using medics or paramedics, with remote support from other medical professionals, who will have specific medical training and be capable of administering drugs, advanced wound treatment, etc.

Question 7

- Primary method – the usual non-emergency method, e.g. ship.
- Secondary method – used when the primary method is unavailable, e.g. lifeboat launched from the rig.
- Tertiary method – heavily reliant on the individual's own effort and used as a last resort when all other methods are unavailable, e.g. putting on lifejackets and survival suits and jumping into the sea.

Question 8

Recovery means that a person who has had to abandon an installation using a secondary or tertiary method is extracted from the sea or vessel by a rescue craft (such as a standby vessel or search and rescue helicopter). **Rescue** is one step beyond recovery – it is recovery but to a place where they can receive medical attention.

Question 9

In such circumstances, the Offshore Installation Manager (OIM) is in overall charge. They will be assisted by two on-scene commanders (one from drilling and one from process), a permit controller, a radio operator and an Offshore Installation Supervisor (OIS).

Element 5: Logistics and Transport Operations

Question 1

International vessels must be registered to a country and abide by its maritime regulations.– this is called **flagging**. For example, UK-registered vessels ("UK Flagged") must comply with the requirements of the UK's Maritime and Coastguard Agency (MCA). These requirements cover (very briefly): certification/approval of vessels, certain equipment on board and crew members; inspection of the vessel (to maintain certification/approval).

Question 2

- Helicopter – depending on weather, location and whether the vessel is fitted with a helideck.
- Transfer basket – transferred from ship-to-ship using the ship's crane.
- Gangways, bridges and accommodation ladders – the usual means of transfer between ship and shore where a ship is moored at port.
- Rope ladder (for pilot transfer) - usually transferred out at sea from a small pilot boat to the ship via a rope ladder hung over the side of the ship.

Question 3

- **Compliance**

  All parties should comply with all applicable national, international, industry and company/contractor requirements for the diving operation.

- **Planning**

  Covers a whole range of activities including such things as: communications, job scope, initial stages of risk assessment, competence, system/equipment checks, emergency planning, change management.

- **Execution**

  Includes: site rules, later stages of risk assessment (on-site), briefings, permit-to-dive.

- **Measuring and Improving**

  Review of the operation and any incidents, and what lessons can be learned.

Question 4

The course must cover both theory and practice and the driver must sit an externally assessed examination – for the classes of goods being carried. This gives him a certificate of competency, which has to be updated at specific intervals.

The course will cover some general aspects of dangerous goods transportation but, for tanker drivers, will also cover tanker-specific issues, such as:

- Vehicle behaviour (e.g. load movement/surge).
- Specific vehicle requirements.
- Filling and discharge.
- Specific rules (approval certificates, marking, placarding, etc).

Question 5

There are two basic reasons:

- Not all roads are suitable for tankers (narrow roads, weak bridges).
- The security threat (terrorism, theft) to the valuable load being carried and its possible use as a terrorist weapon.